MW00657981

Praise for *Tapped Out for College Students: Stress Relief Using EFT*

In *Tapped out for College Students: Stress Relief Using EFT,* Kelley and Becki have created a much-needed resource for busy students, giving them an easy-to-follow format for success at school. The authors give important background about Emotional Freedom Techniques or EFT, without overwhelming students with too much information. They quickly get to the important scripts, designed to facilitate stress relief. Each section of the book is broken into the most common topics college students may encounter. The scripts in each section guide the students through the EFT process, or tapping, allowing them to quickly release the negative emotions holding them back.

Studies have shown that stress levels at college are on the rise, yet, until now, students haven't had an easy means to cope. This book empowers students to have control over their stress. This is an awesome resource for every college student. Definitely a must-have.

Nick Ortner
New York Times* Bestselling Author of *The Tapping Solution

"Rarely do you get such a comprehensive resource for students about to go to college and those who are attending college. This is more than a must have book for college students and I recommend that all parents provide this book for their college student as a resource to help them when they cannot be there. It's a 'be prepared' resource, a 'first aid' resource and a 'solutions' resource. Authors, Becki and Kelley have hit the nail on the head with this book, providing practical solutions to so many potential issues that college students may face, from tapping scripts to hotline numbers to call. They address overwhelm, homesickness, procrastination, homework, confusion, working a job, socialising, dating, budgeting, depression, fear of not graduating, substance abuse, exams, interviews, internships and so much more. This book is also helpful for parents to read before they pack it off to college with their new college student. Read *Tapped out for College Students* now! It's the best resource a college student could possibly have."

Jenny Johnston
EFT Universe Trainer, Founder of Quantum EFT,
Best Selling Author of *Tapping into Past Lives*
www.jennyjohnston.com.au, www.quantumeft.com.au

I remember vividly that first time I met Becki and Kelley at my EFT Certification training in Concord, NH. I could see the passion and excitement they were bringing to the table, and their fantastic ability to soak up what they were learning and immediately implement it into their self-work and client work. I knew right there and then that I was watching two EFT experts in the making. The book you are holding in your hands is proof of their expertise and dedication to excellence. Since that first weekend, Becki and Kelley have taken numerous EFT workshops and have received extensive mentoring to be able to do their high-level work with college students. Follow their suggestions step by step. Don't just read, but actually do the exercises they suggest. It will make all the difference in your college career and how you approach your future life.

Ingrid Dinter
Accredited Certified EFT Master Trainer, Speaker, EFT Consultant, and Coauthor of *EFT for PTSD*

I am honored to provide a review for the new book, "Tapped Out for College Students; Stress Relief Using EFT" written by my EFT Colleagues, Kelley Pryor Amrein and Becki Stevens. I know that when our minds and bodies are stressed, we don't make good decisions, and college is hugely stressful. College students really need EFT, an easy-to-learn self-help tool, to reduce their stress so they can enjoy their college experience. The book is very well organized and easy-to-follow. Students can go right to the area they need in the moment and simply follow the script. Since we are all different, Kelley and Becki encourage students to tap on the truth of their emotions. Every situation that may be causing a college student stress is listed, and a tapping script is provided that really covers the subject! This book is a must-have for every college student! I look forward to their next book in the series.

Barbara E. Belmont
AAMET Accredited Certified
Advanced EFT Practitioner, Belmont Coaching and Consulting Services, www.barbaraebelmont.com

The more I delved into *Tapped Out for College Students* the more excited I got! This is a fantastic tool for college students. I have witnessed how the stress of transitioning to college life can overwhelming at times for most young adults. I hear parents wish they had more tools to help. This easy to understand and thorough gift will become the most valuable book in a college student's library. I intend to buy one for each of my wellness patients as they head off to college!

Dr. Jenny Bruck
Wellness Chiropractor
Author of the book *52 Vitality Tools*
Host of the podcast *For the Health of It*

College is stressful. At least that is true for everyone I have ever met. Not only are we transitioning from an established life, surrounded by family and friends, we are learning to manage our own schedules, to prioritize, to take care of ourselves and to navigate a new and sometimes daunting social life. As college students, we do this while simultaneously dealing with a much greater work load, complex subject matter and the pressure to succeed when we (or our parents) are investing a lot of money towards our education. It seems that the common expectation is that we will somehow just know how to figure all of this out ourselves after a day of orientation and a few minutes spent with our academic advisor. But, the truth is, that most of us are quite unprepared to handle all the different factors involved in higher learning.

Fortunately, Kelley Pryor Amrein and Becki Stevens offer practical solutions to bring some blessed relief and address the many challenges we face during this crucial time. *Tapped Out for College Students: Stress Relief Using EFT*, is the perfect combination of straightforward, understandable, and thorough. It covers the obstacles that we often face as students and explains easy and effective techniques and tools for overcoming them. I found the way that Kelley and Becki break everything down into the categories of Because, Emotion(s), Sensation(s), and Distress, or BESD, makes the process of tapping even more accessible and doable.

I particularly love how the book is divided into chapters that examine each major issue and offers clear and concise examples of exactly how to manage every challenge, and even wisely includes a section for when it seems like nothing is working. I certainly wish this book existed when I was navigating college and graduate school! As an EFT practitioner, I know how effective tapping has been to shift so many things in my life, including procrastination and overwhelm. If I had the tools that Becki and Kelley offer here when I was a student, I suspect I wouldn't have needed to spend 6 years earning my BFA, or pulled nearly as many stressful last minute marathons writing papers in seminary. While this book is written for students, so much of it can apply to the rest of us, too. I had come down with a lingering head cold while reading this book, and even though my college days are behind me, I found the tapping script for being sick very helpful. Knowing a number of people who'll be college bound in the next few years, I look forward to gifting copies of this book to each of them.

Rev. Jennifer Elizabeth Moore
Wholistic Mentor & Creator of the Empathic Woman System
empathicwoman.com

I am thrilled that Kelley and Becki have created this valuable resource for college students!! Not many know this about me, but many years ago, I worked at an exclusive residential high school. The students were females from all over the globe and I distinctly remember the weekend when they were taking the SATs. The girls were literally sick and emotionally distraught, filled with fear and panic. The amount of pressure these girls put on themselves was shocking to me. I remember sitting with a couple of them and just listening to them cry and share how important this test was for their future and for their families. My heart was broken for them and I wished I had more resources at that time to support them in reducing this emotional charge and to give them another perspective. Becki and Kelley's book, "Tapped Out for College Students", can be a great resource for students, allowing them to feel more empowered and clear at each stage of their college life journey. Many people who begin tapping look for scripts to guide them through the process, and this book provides numerous great examples and covers the many different challenges common to college students. Tapping itself has helped so many, and I urge anyone who is looking for a way to respond to the challenges of life to learn how to tap and work with a tapping professional.

Kimberly Francano
Achieving Greatness Coach, Tapping Expert, Speaker of Inspiration
Kimberlyfrancano.com

ISBN-10: 0-9986153-0-7
ISBN-13: 978-0-9986153-0-1

Tapped Out for College Students

Tapped Out for College Students

Stress Relief Using EFT

Kelley Pryor Amrein
and
Becki Stevens

Dedication

We dedicate this book to all college students and hope that within these pages you discover the ease and freedom offered by Emotional Freedom Techniques or EFT.

Becki's dedication

I dedicate this book to my family, Brian, Toby & Josey, for their support, patience and love during this whole process. I would also like to dedicate this to Janelle, for introducing me to EFT, which changed how I live my life, and for her never ending encouragement.

Kelley's dedication

To my family, Jim, Andrew, Shannon and Jonathon. Your love grounds me, your support keeps me going, and your sense of humor fills my life with laughter. You all are the best.

Disclaimer

Please read before continuing further:

Tapped Out for College Students: Stress Relief Using EFT (*Tapped Out*) includes suggestions, techniques, exercises and ideas that are educational in nature and are provided as general information, to be used solely for the reader's own self-care and self-improvement. No suggestion, technique, exercise or idea expressed in this book is intended to diagnose, treat, cure, or prevent any disease or psychological/mental health disorder. Consequently, this book does not provide medical diagnoses or offer cures. This book is not meant to replace standard medical care and/or mental health care or counseling.

Tapped Out is a step-by-step guide containing information about the energy therapy called Emotional Freedom Techniques (EFT) or tapping. EFT is based on a combination of ancient Chinese Acupressure techniques and talk therapy. EFT allows a person to balance his or her energy system by tapping gently with their fingertips on specific meridian points located under the skin on the face and body. Using EFT allows a person to address the emotions and/or situations creating stress and imbalance in his or her energy system.

While there is a growing body of scientific research indicating the effectiveness of EFT, especially in the reduction of stress, EFT is still considered experimental. Therefore, the reader assumes full responsibility for any and all risk associated with reading *Tapped Out* and using EFT. If any distress or discomfort, either physical and/or emotional, is experienced, the reader is advised to stop and seek professional medical or mental health care, as appropriate.

While the authors of *Tapped Out* are experienced, certified EFT practitioners, they are not licensed health care providers. They do not guarantee the outcome regarding the reading of *Tapped Out* or the use of EFT for an individual for any particular purpose.

The authors and publishers of this book are not responsible for any adverse effects or consequences resulting from the use of any or all suggestions, techniques, exercises, or ideas contained within the book. By continuing to read *Tapped Out*, the reader agrees to fully release, indemnify and hold harmless the authors of *Tapped Out* from any claim or liability and for any damage or injury whatsoever that the reader may incur in relation to the use of the information presented in *Tapped Out*.

By continuing to read *Tapped Out* you agree to all of the above.

Contents

Foreword

There I was, once again, sitting in my dorm room, looking at my calculus homework swimming over the page...and the next thing I knew, I was staring into space. I had zoned out. Or, you could say I'd "zoned in" to a strange space that felt like a mixture of being frozen in fear, worries racing through my head, and being strangely blank, unmotivated, and unable to focus. I sat there quietly, sometimes watching my roommate actually study, while time rushed by and, eventually, ran out.

Freshman year of engineering school was tough. Not because I wasn't smart enough or the work was too hard, but because I didn't understand how the pressure and anxiety of school was affecting me, and I had no way to handle the stress. Because of this, I struggled, making school harder than it needed to be. As a result, my self-esteem suffered many unnecessary hits that took years to heal.

Fast forward eighteen years and a successful career working in several high-tech companies, to the time when I found Tapping or Emotional Freedom Techniques. EFT was a revelation to me, allowing me to both understand the workings of the psychological fight-flight-or- freeze response, as well as providing me with an amazing technique that actually worked to physically shut it off.

Armed with my new understanding and this powerful tool, I was able to make massive changes in my life and career as I left corporate America to build my own coaching business. I watched in amazement as my clients, using EFT, shifted years of pain, trauma, limiting beliefs, and anxiety before my eyes, and then were able to move into inspired action! Likewise, I observed the changes in myself with equal amazement. With Tapping, I was able to do things I never, EVER imagined I would have the courage to do, and then say "yes" to more.

Over the years, I have had the honor and pleasure of being part of the healing and transformation of thousands of people in my programs and through my coach training programs!

But, one of the most rewarding things I've had the privilege of doing, is to lend help to my own daughters, nieces and nephews as they navigate the stages in their lives from first grade, through SATS; from sports, to stage fright, through college and even to taking the Bar examination!

Like all kids and young adults, they have big dreams, pressures and worries that can sometimes feel overwhelming. Miraculously, twenty minutes of Tapping allows them to lift away the overwhelm and return to their natural enthusiasm and lightness of being.

One of the MOST common ways these mini sessions end is with them saying, "I have this friend who really needs this…." Or sometimes… "I showed all my friends tapping…."

Unfortunately, as they grow from children to college age, their worries and pressures become more sophisticated and, therefore, more intense. We have an epidemic of young people with anxiety who don't really understand what it is and why it is being triggered, nor how to easily be free of their stress. At risk is their confidence, self-esteem, and their ability to continue on their path to success. That risk is compounded by their increased access to alcohol and drugs, which all seem to temporarily give relief to anxiety and self-doubt.

This is why I am so excited Kelley and Becki have created this incredible resource totally focused on college-age young adults and the very specific issues they are dealing with.

Kelley and Becki have thoughtfully constructed this guidebook as a resource, so that it can be utilized easily and quickly by a college kid running on empty and with "no time". They have minimized the history, data, and science of Tapping typically covered in the many other books out there, and instead focused on a recipe book of sorts, dialed in to very specific issues.

This makes the book incredibly user friendly and inviting. Just a look through the chapter headings will let anyone in college quickly see that this book is for clearly for them!

The authors have also taken the time to go beyond the pressures of exams and self-doubt, and included social and relationship issues, sleep, money worries, and even food cravings. Clearly, they know who they are passionate about helping!

This book will truly be a gift for a high school or college-aged young adult, both in learning the actual tapping technique to shift their state of stress and anxiety, and in understanding how external and internal pressures create stress.

And through this, I believe they will better understand themselves, their automatic reactions, and discover their own ability to shift their perspectives each day, as well as their destinies.

Imagine: empowering a generation of young people with the tools to clear away the debilitating effects of anxiety and self-doubt, allowing them to thrive as their unique, powerful, and gifted selves!

Bravo to Becki and Kelley for pouring their hearts and expertise into this important work!

Margaret M Lynch
www.margaretmlynch.com
Speaker, Transformational Coach, Author of the book,
Tapping Into Wealth **(Penguin Random House)**

Introduction

"I wish there was an EFT book for college students." I said this at the end of 2015 when my colleague and friend, Becki Stevens, and I, were meeting to catch up, do a little tapping, and discuss our coaching businesses. Becki had just opened an office and was busy establishing herself as a first-class EFT or Emotional Freedom Techniques, coach. I was about to follow suit in January of 2016. We were both working to establish our niches in the EFT world, both passionate about finding clients with whom to share this amazing tool. Sharing our struggles and our successes, as well as EFT or Tapping, provided the support that we needed as new entrepreneurs.

Becki had shown me a few books she used as guides when facilitating EFT with children. The books were great because they provided parents with young children a tool for alleviating the stress their kids experienced in school, with friends, and at home. I was frustrated because my college-age daughter, several thousand miles from home, was struggling with the stress of university and a chronic illness, and I struggled to know how to help her. She was open to using EFT, but, given the typical college student's schedule, it was difficult for us to connect if she needed guidance while she tapped. So, I wished for a book that covered topics pertinent to her experience; one that would guide her in tapping when we couldn't tap together.

"Let's write one," Becki responded, and this book, *Tapped Out for College Students, Stress Relief Using EFT*, was born.

Becki and I put together a survey to identify the biggest stressors facing college students. We also had the privilege of meeting with college students to ask questions and introduce Emotional Freedom Techniques (EFT) or tapping. We spoke and tapped with many students, gathered the results of our survey, began to compile our findings and determine what tapping scripts should be presented in the book, and finally, once again, we garnered the help of college students in our area to read and provide feedback on the first draft of this work.

Of course, Becki and I remember our college days, although they were more than a few years ago. Much has changed and the many new challenges and opportunities of today add new layers of stress to the university experience. We hope that this book is an ever-evolving body of work; one that changes with feedback and input from the students who experience it, so that the information shared remains applicable to university students over time and through the inevitable changes in the college landscape. We also hope that parents, high-school teachers, and counselors on both high school and college campuses will read the book and use it with their students. EFT is a technique that can be easily learned and quickly put to use as a self-help tool, to alleviate stress, clear tension, reduce pain and induce relaxation and calm.

About the Authors

Before we get into the background of EFT and exactly what this technique entails, which you will find in Chapter One, we would like to introduce ourselves.

I'm Kelley Pryor Amrein. I discovered EFT in 2007 while living in India. I took two weekend EFT courses, the first in 2007 and the second in 2008, with an EFT teacher from Mumbai. Using EFT, I was able to clear some long-held traumas and limiting beliefs: things I had forgotten or had not realized still impacted my life. After my family returned to the States, I continued to use EFT for myself and my family. Then, in 2014, I decided it was time to take EFT to another level in my life and I joined an EFT training program where I met Becki. I am not only an EFT coach but also a writer, traveler and yoga teacher. I enjoy using EFT in conjunction with these various modalities, and I find that tapping blends with every aspect of my career and personal life. I am a mom of three; one through college, one mid-way, and one about to embark on the university experience. I have witnessed the stress they have experienced; received numerous long-distance calls when classes are tough or illness hits. I know this book will make a difference, and that is why I am passionate about this project and working with Becki to spread tapping to college campuses. I believe that ten minutes of EFT in the morning translates into a day of more peace and calm; a true representation of time well spent that actually adds quality time to your day.

I'm Becki Stevens and I was first introduced to EFT by a close friend who had noticed that I was having a very difficult time getting over an upsetting event. After tapping for just a few minutes, I felt such relief, that I immediately started researching EFT. The more I learned about EFT and used tapping to release my limiting beliefs, the more I wanted to share this amazing, easy technique with others. Having been a stay-at-home mom for twelve years, I was ready for a professional purpose and EFT Coaching is my calling. I met Kelley at my first EFT training event in Concord, New Hampshire. We have continued working together and agree that writing a book would be a great way to spread the word about EFT. Since we are both moms, first and foremost, we immediately gravitated towards writing a book that benefits young adults, like the ones in our lives. The perfect answer for us is this book; we are excited to share the benefits EFT can have with college students. Giving students the power and knowledge to relieve their own stress is not only helpful in school, but in life outside of school, as well.

About This Book

This book is not intended to provide an in-depth explanation of EFT, although we will provide information about EFT and how it works as well as present the most recent scientific findings supporting the effectiveness of this technique. What we want to do is give college students an immediate process for handling stress and we know that, after class is over, the last thing a student wants or needs is another dry text-book-style summary to digest. So we promise not to burden you with too much detail. We will, however, provide an Appendix with additional resources for further reading in case anyone wants to delve more deeply into Emotional Freedom Techniques and why it is so effective.

This book is also not intended as a replacement for the professional medical care of a licensed physician or mental health practitioner. We often refer to Appendix C where we have compiled a list of resources if you find that the you are unable to handle your situation. Please, also remember that your campus Health and Wellness Center provides professional counseling and health care services. Go there first if what you are experiencing is life-threatening, threatens your mental well-being, is violent or uncontrollable, or feels too overwhelming to handle alone.

We have broken this book into sections based on what you encounter in college. The **Introduction** provides an overview of EFT as well as a how-to on tapping and the tapping points.

Each of the next sections contain tapping scripts designed to help you tap through the stresses of college. **Section One** scripts cover Classes and Homework issues. **Section Two** scripts deal with Grades and Exams. The scripts in **Section Three** are about Time Management. In **Section Four** we cover Relationships. **Section Five** scripts guide you as you tap about Money. In **Section Six** you will find scripts concerning Physical and Emotional Health. For scripts to guide you in Transitions, head to **Section Seven**. **Section Eight** scripts help you cope with The Real World. Finally, in **Section Nine** you will find several Miscellaneous scripts that defied categorization.

The **Table of Contents** is a good place to start as you look for the right script to help you with a specific problem. In order to help you create a personal tapping script, we have included some blank templates at the back of the book in **Appendix B**. Filled-in versions of these sample scripts are found throughout the book.

Appendix C provides a list of resources for your use. We will reference Appendix C throughout the book if we want to let you know about additional information to augment the scripts. In Appendix C, we have included the books and online resources we have found useful as we researched. We have also included some phone numbers for quick access to help if you find you need support for a particular issue.

Now it is time to Tap It Out!

Becki and Kelley

What is Emotional Freedom Techniques or EFT

Emotional Freedom Techniques (EFT) is a do-it-yourself healing tool that alleviates stress, reduces physical pain and increases your potential for success. It is a non-invasive energy therapy using gentle finger tapping on specific meridian points beneath the surface of the skin. The meridians come from Chinese medicine. They create pathways through which Qi (*chee*), or energy, flows to all parts of the human body.[1] The meridians form the basis of the practice of acupuncture.[2] This idea of energy flowing in the body is, then, certainly not a new one, and it is this theory that EFT works from. In fact, EFT is often termed acupuncture without the needles.

So, how does EFT actually work? EFT's magic rests in its ability to smooth out disruptions in your energy system. EFT was developed in the 1990s by a Stanford University-trained engineer named Gary Craig. Gary Craig was a student of the forefather of EFT, Roger Callahan, who had previously developed a system of meridian tapping called TFT or Thought Field Therapy. Gary Craig took TFT, a process which used tapping on specific meridian points depending on the emotion you were feeling, and simplified it. He designed the system to stimulate the major meridian points in an unchanging sequence. It does not matter what emotion you are feeling because the tapping remains the same whether you are experiencing anger, fear, sadness or pain. By tapping on the points identified in EFT, you are able to access all the major energy circuits and find relief.

The underpinning of Gary Craig's work is his discovery statement, which says, "The cause of all negative emotions is a disruption in the body's energy system."[3] Using EFT, we tap on the negative emotions from a specific event, for instance the overwhelming stress we feel due to an upcoming examination. Tapping on the stress, the negative emotion, allows the emotion to be released and the energy disruption is then straightened out. This release of the negative allows the flow of positive energy back into your life. With the brain no longer feeling overloaded you are then able to retrieve the information needed to ace the exam.

Here comes the science part of this explanation. Part of the human brain is ancient and has been in operation, working to keep our species alive, for thousands of years. The limbic brain is the oldest, most primitive part of the brain and a part of the limbic brain is a small, almond shaped area called the amygdala. The amygdala is the part of the brain triggered when you are in danger, the relay station that sends out the message for your fight or flight response to kick in. When this response is activated, it signals the body of danger and the hormones adrenaline and cortisol are released. In ancient times, when this part of our brain developed, it was essential for our survival.[4] The release of adrenaline and cortisol fueled our ancestors who were able to flee rather than being eaten by a tiger for lunch. Good for them then, and for us; we're still here, after all.

You might wonder how this relates to your exam. After all, you are not running from a beast. Interestingly, however, this primitive portion of your brain, the amygdala, cannot detect real "tiger" danger from imagined "stress" danger. Your body senses exam stress as a danger and releases the same fight or flight hormones our ancestors needed to stay alive. Keep in mind that our ancestors did not have stress on a daily or even hourly basis like we do. The brain reacts to this modern-day stress just as it did to the tiger stress; it causes adrenaline and cortisol to be released.[5]

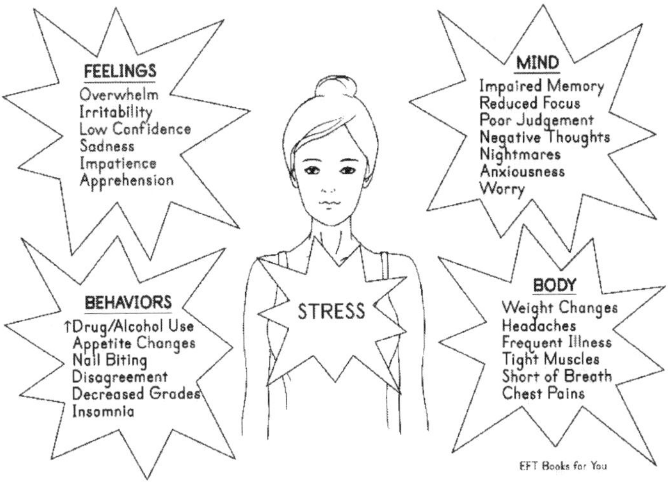

Diagram 1

Cortisol has been deemed public enemy number one. When cortisol floods our bodies, we have to physically move to get rid of it. But when there is no tiger to fight or flee from, when the danger is, instead, exam stress, all the stress hormones in our bodies have nowhere to go. The cortisol hangs out and wreaks havoc on our minds and bodies, weakening our immune system, causing damage on a cellular level, leaving us vulnerable to infection.[6] Tapping on the meridian points calms the fight or flight response, allowing our bodies to relax and cortisol levels to drop.[7]

Dr. Dawson Church has done several studies on how tapping affects our bodies. In one randomized controlled study conducted by Dr. Church and his peers, cortisol levels and psychological symptoms of eighty-three patients were tested before and after treatment. The patients were divided into three groups. One group received no therapy but only an hour of rest. Another group received one hour of conventional talk therapy. The third group had a one-hour session of EFT tapping. Subsequent testing revealed that the symptoms in the EFT group decreased more than within the other groups and cortisol levels also dropped significantly. The group which received talk therapy had a reduction in cortisol of 14% while the group receiving EFT had an average reduction in cortisol of 24%.[8]

Another interesting study was released in *Energy Psychology Journal* in 2013. In this study, a group of college students was divided into two groups to work on various emotional responses using either mindfulness techniques or EFT. The purpose of this work was to determine whether EFT worked or was, instead, simply a placebo effect. The research found that the students using EFT experienced a greater increase in positive emotions and a greater decrease in negative emotions. The students did not experience any significant change in emotions using mindfulness techniques. The conclusion of the researchers was that EFT is not a placebo and can be effective for students experiencing emotional conditions.[9]

EFT has been shown to be effective time and again in scientific studies. It is not a placebo but is an effective energy psychology technique that calms your amygdala, causing a reduction of the stress hormones in your body. Reducing stress may result in relief from physical pain and emotional suffering because stress is often an underlying part of any problems you are facing.[10]

As you tap on the meridian points used in EFT, you will be saying negative statements. You may feel that saying something negative only reinforces its negative power. Actually, that is not true. Imagine that you fail your most important exam of the year. Of course, this has an impact on your GPA and you know you and your parents will not be pleased. So, you decide not to tell your parents about this grade and hope that it all goes away. After all, you are an adult and no one is going to send a note to your folks tattling on you.

Your plan works fine until, somehow, the truth comes out. Maybe you never recovered from that grade. Perhaps it had further reaching repercussions than you had anticipated. Whatever the reason, your parents find out. Now what do you do? Perhaps you are relieved. After all, a secret is a big burden to carry. That is how it is with stress and negative emotions we hold inside. They don't go away until we face them. There is a sense of relief when the secret, or the emotions, are finally revealed.

Tapping is a little like revealing the secret. You cannot feel truly good inside until you face the negative emotions holding you back. Once you recognize and acknowledge the negative it can finally go away.[11]

We follow the expression of our negative emotions with a statement of acceptance. This statement could be as simple as "I accept myself." The acceptance statement is important because, in order to heal you have to accept, or be okay with yourself, right where you are at the moment.[12] This can be a difficult statement for some people to make. If you are having a tough time saying "I accept myself," use a different statement, one that may be less triggering, such as "I am okay" or "I am open to accepting myself" or "I accept the situation and am open to change."

EFT works energetically by releasing the disruptions in your energy system to quickly and easily reduce stress, ease pain, and return you to a calm state. EFT is an energy therapy and, as such, allows your system to heal naturally and easily. It's time to learn how you can use this technique in your life.

How to Use EFT to Tap It Out!

EFT is easy to master. It doesn't require any special tools, just your fingers and your words. With a little practice, you'll be tapping away emotions like stress, anger, sadness and fear as well as physical sensations, like pain or butterflies in your stomach, in no time. This part of the book is designed to give you an introduction into the mechanics of tapping. Here, we'll show you where you tap, called the tapping points. We'll talk about how you measure your tapping success. And we will tell you what to say by providing sample tapping scripts. When you are ready, you can add your own words. This is easy and we will take you through the process step-by-step. Soon you will be tapping it out, on your own, like a pro, whenever and wherever.

The BESD: Because, Emotions, Sensations, and Distress

There are four quick steps to follow before you tap; 1) Discover the ***Because***, the situation that has triggered a response or emotion; 2) Identify the ***Emotion*** associated with the Because; 3) Notice any physical ***Sensations*** associated with the Emotion(s) you've identified; 4) Assess your current level of ***Distress***.

Before you begin a tapping session, it's helpful if you can take a couple of minutes to sit quietly and evaluate what's going on. Relax and take a deep breath. Ask yourself what's troubling you right now. It is possible that you will be in a public place and your circumstances may not lend themselves to this part. And sometimes the situation and the associated emotions are easy to figure out and you can start tapping immediately. This is especially true once you've tapped a few times. But if you aren't quite sure what's bothering you, try to find a place to be still and tune into yourself.

Maybe the first thing that comes to mind is the fight you had with your significant other or your roommate. Or maybe you have a test coming up and you have no idea how you're going to get all the studying done that you know you need to do. You've identified what's bugging you. We call this the *because*, the situation that *triggers* an emotional response. Once you know the *because*, you can find the *emotion* that relates. Let's break this out further.

As an example, we will use the upcoming exam as the *because*. This examination is big; it counts for fifty percent of your grade. It is the one covering a million chapters and pages of notes. Yikes. The test is the *because*, but what is the *emotion* you feel when you think about that test? Maybe the *emotion* is fear. Maybe it's stress or tension and a resulting sense of overwhelm. All of this is important information to have before you begin to tap.

Let's talk a minute about the physical *sensations* that might accompany the emotional reaction to your *because* situation. Maybe you don't associate your pounding headache or sore shoulder muscles with your emotions, but guess what, they are definitely related. Mel Pohl, MD, FASAM, has found that emotional pain contributes to the chronic pain his patients experience. He believes that approximately 20 percent of chronic pain is sensory but 80 percent of the pain is actually emotional.[13] So pay close attention to any physical *sensations* that arise before or during your tapping. Also, notice if any physical issues get better after EFT. You might recognize that your shoulders feel looser or that nasty headache is gone. Yep. EFT can take care of that and more.

We're almost ready to tap, but before we get started let's assess the level of *distress* you feel associated with the exam and the corresponding emotion. Because stress is a common emotional response to test-taking, let's use stress in this example. To assess your level of *distress*, once again take a moment to tune in to your body and ask yourself how bad the stress is on a scale of 0 to 10. Zero equals no stress, which is the goal you would like to achieve through tapping. Ten equals intense stress, as intense as it can get. This scale is called the Subjective Units of Distress or SUD in EFT. In this book, we will simply refer to it as *Distress*.

No two people respond to something in the same way. Plus, you may feel like your stress is a 5 one moment and it bumps up to an 8 in the next. Additionally, you may feel something is an 8 while someone else may feel it is a 3. EFT empowers you to take control of your emotional response to any situation. It's okay. Be honest, acknowledge your feelings, and tap them out. Your goal with tapping is to reduce your distress level to a point that it's no big deal.

To review:

1. Determine the trigger, the ***Because***
2. Identify the corresponding ***Emotion***
3. Notice if you have any related physical ***Sensations*** (it's okay if you don't)
4. Assess your level of ***Distress*** from 0 to 10

The Tapping Points: Relief at your Fingertips

We want to introduce you to the main tapping points you will be using in EFT. These points comprise what is called the **Basic Recipe** in EFT. You will use two to three fingers to gently tap on each point. In the **Basic Recipe,** you gently and continuously tap on these points four to nine times with your fingertips. It is fine to tap longer on each point; allow your instincts, and what feels good, to guide you. The tapping points used in the **Basic Recipe** are illustrated in the accompanying picture. (See Diagram 2) To see a demonstration of the tapping points, go to our website, http://eftbooksforyou.com/2017straightA

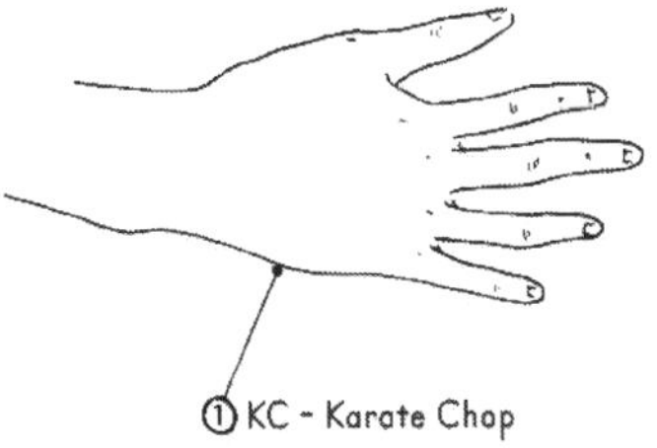

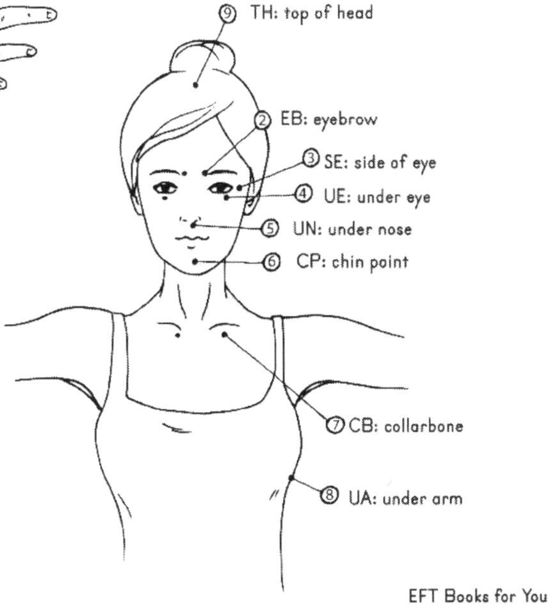

Basic Recipe

KC – Karate Chop
EB – Eyebrow
SE – Side of eye
UE – Under eye
UN – Under nose
CP – Chin Point
CB – Collarbone
UA – Under arm
TH – Top of Head

Diagram 2

To start each new topic, begin tapping on the **Karate Chop (KC)** point. The **Karate Chop** point is located on the outside of the hand below the joint of the little finger; on the fleshy area you would use in martial arts to hit in a karate chop fashion. You tap on the Karate Chop point using what is called a **set-up statement**, which always begins with **Even though** and ends with a statement of acceptance, such as **I accept myself**. You may tap with either hand. You can even switch hands midway through. Continue to tap gently on this point while you say the **set-up statement** three times. The set-up statement can be written and stated in free-flow dialogue. This is, perhaps, the one time when the written word is structured to fit the way you speak and grammatical correctness is not mandatory.

Here is an example of a **set-up statement.** Other set-up statements throughout the book may be longer and more detailed. Again, let the words flow and do not worry about grammatical perfection. This is your time to vent your feelings.

Even though** I feel sad, **I accept myself.

Next you tap on the rest of the points in the **Basic Recipe** as you repeat a **reminder phrase**. As you say the **reminder phrase**, you move to each point on the face and torso, again using two or three fingers to lightly tap. You may tap with your right hand, your left hand or both hands as some points are found on both sides of your face or body. Here is an example of the reminder phrase.

This sadness…

You can tap on each point saying the exact same reminder phrase throughout the tapping. You may also change the reminder phrase on each point to encompass a more complex issue. You will see examples of this throughout the book.

Say the **reminder phrase** tapping on the points in the order listed:

1. **Eyebrow (EB)** where the eyebrow starts at the inside of the eye
2. **Side of the Eye (SE)** at the outside corner of the eye on the boney area
3. **Under the Eye (UE)** below the pupil, on the bone of the eye socket
4. **Under the Nose (UN)** In the groove between your nose and upper lip
5. **Chin Point (CP)** in the crease of the chin, not the point of the chin
6. **Collarbone (CB)** located an inch below the collarbone

7. **Under the Arm (UA)** about four inches below the armpit, across from the center of the chest, where the bra circles the ribs for women
8. **Top of the Head (TH)** a bit back from the center and generally in line with the top of your ears.

Each time you tap on the points from your eyebrow to the top of your head is considered one round. Stop after each round or two to check in and see what your level of distress is. You can also tap several rounds of the **basic recipe** continuously before you stop if it feels good to just keep tapping. Then assess where you are when you feel ready to pause.

You might notice, as you tap, that your original emotion shifts to a new emotion. For example, you may start out feeling stressed about an upcoming exam and, after tapping a round or two, you might become aware that the stress has given way to fear about the exam, or anger that you have so much studying to do.

In the following example, two rounds of tapping will be illustrated with a third round showing the change to a new emotion after your distress levels lower and a new emotion surfaces. Know that this shift is actually a good thing and allows you to work through all the emotions you might feel around a situation.

Just as emotions can shift during tapping, so can the physical sensations you might experience. As you begin to tap, you may have identified a particular physical pain and included that in your tapping. After you tap a few rounds and pause to reassess your distress level, you may notice that the original pain is gone but a new physical sensation has shown up. It is fine to tap on the new sensation when you continue. In EFT, we call this "chasing the pain."

Finally, you can tap on physical pain without any accompanying emotions. This can help when you cannot pinpoint or voice your emotions; because sometimes you just don't know why you are feeling stressed. You simply feel it. EFT is a great tool to use to alleviate pain like headaches, neck aches, muscle pain, even stomach aches. Tapping helps your body to relax and release the pain. You might even find an emotion attached to the pain as you tap, so add that in as you go along.

Sample Scripts

It is time to work with some sample scripts so you feel more comfortable diving into the book to tap on your own. Each sample script will identify the *Because*, the *Emotion*, and the *Sensations* you might have by underlining each of these parts of the script. Be sure that you note your level of *Distress* before you begin. To see a demonstration of how to tap through a script using the Basic Recipe, go to our website. www.eftbooksforyou.com/2017straightA

Sample Script 1 Exam Stress

1. **Because:** I have an upcoming exam, I might fail or get a bad grade
2. **Emotion:** Stress
3. **Sensation:** Stomach upset
4. **Distress:** 7

Karate Chop or **KC**: **Even though** I am stressed because I might fail the exam, and my stomach is upset just thinking about it, **I completely accept myself**. (You will repeat this phrase three times while tapping)

Tapping on the eyebrow or **EB:** I am feeling stressed

Tapping on side of eye or **SE:** Because I have an exam coming up

Tapping under the eye or **UE:** I am really stressed because I might fail the exam

Tapping under the nose or **UN:** My stomach is upset thinking about the exam

Tapping in chin crease or **CP:** This stress

Tapping on collarbone or **CB:** I feel the stress in my stomach

Tapping under the arm or **UA:** All this stress because I might fail the exam

Tapping top of the head or **TH:** All this stress because I might fail the exam is making my stomach upset

Sample Script 2 Exam Stress

Here is the same script filled in with slightly different words. See how the wording can vary yet still contain the same basic elements; the *Because*, the *Emotion*, and the *Sensation*, if applicable.

KC: **Even though** I am feeling stressed because I have an exam coming up in two days, and my stomach is upset just thinking about it, **I completely accept myself and how I feel**. (repeat three times)

EB: I am feeling stressed
SE: Because my exam is in two days
UE: I am really stressed because I have so much studying to do
UN: I might fail or get a bad grade
CP: This stress
CB: It is so strong that it is making my stomach hurt
UA: All this stress because I might not get a good grade or even pass

TH: All this stress because of this exam and I feel it, my stomach is upset

Sample Script 3 Exam Stress

This script changes the emotion and adds to the because or trigger so that you can see how your feelings might shift as you tap.

1. **Because**: Exam coming up in two days plus so much homework. I have too much to do
2. **Emotion:** Anger
3. **Sensation:** Tightness in my chest
4. **Distress:** 8

KC: Even though I'm angry because I have an exam in two days plus so much homework and I feel it in my body, my chest feels tight, **I accept myself and how I feel**. (repeat three times)

EB: I'm angry
SE: Because I have an exam in two days
UE: Plus so much homework to do as well
UN: My chest feels tight because I am so angry
CP: All this anger because I have too much to do
CB: This anger is so strong
UA: I feel this anger in my chest
TH: All this anger because I have too much to do and I feel it in my body, my chest feels tight

There are many more scripts in the book. Each one is filled in, just like the sample scripts here. Below each script in the book you will find sections called **Optional Because** and **Optional Emotions** with alternative suggestions for triggers and the resulting emotions. Don't forget to add in any physical **Sensation** you might be experiencing as a result of your situation, keeping in mind that physical pain like headache is often related to your emotional state. For more blank scripts, you can check out **Appendix B**. We have provided several samples to help you set up your personal EFT session.

The Hand Points

Hand Points

KC – Karate Chop
TH - Thumb
IF – Index Finger
MF – Middle Finger
LF – Little Finger
GP - Gamut Point

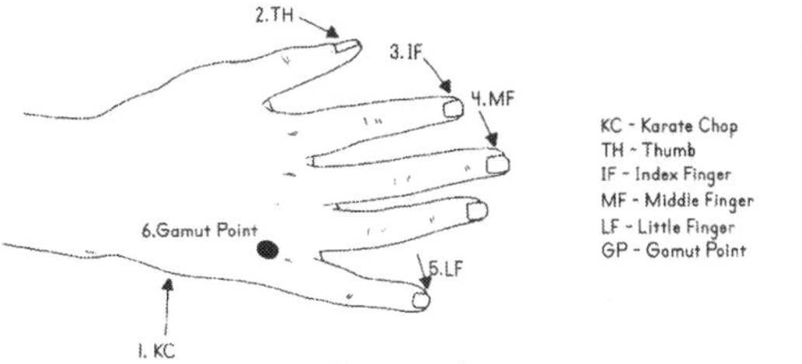

Diagram 3

When you want to release intense emotions without others noticing, you can use the hand points. To easily find the finger points, begin by holding either one of your hands out in front of you with the thumb pointing up, as if you were about to shake someone's hand. As in the Basic Recipe, you begin the tapping on the **Karate Chop (KC)** point, which is at the bottom of your extended hand. Your next point is your **Thumb (TH),** on the uppermost part of your thumb on the outside edge of your nail. The next point is the **Index Finger (IF)**, again on the uppermost part of the finger at the side of the nail. Move next to the **Middle Finder (MF)** and then **Little Finger (LF)**, always at the uppermost part of the finger on the outside edge of the nail.

The final tapping point on the hand is called the **Gamut Point. (GP)**. Make a loose fist with your hand and put the index finger of you opposite hand between your pinky and ring knuckles on the back of your hand. Slide your index finger up about an inch on top of the back of your hand toward your wrist. You'll probably feel a groove there. This is your **Gamut Point**. This point covers your ring finger point. You can tap this gamut point or rub it. Finally, you can finish tapping the round on your **Karate Chop** point. Continue tapping on the points until your intensity reduces. This method is especially useful in social situations and in times when you don't want others to see you tapping. As you tap you will THINK the words rather than say them out loud. To see a tapping demonstration using the Hand Points, go to our website. www.eftbooksforyou.com/2017straightA

Here is a sample script for Exam Stress using the **Hand Points**.

1. **Because:** I have an upcoming exam, I might fail or get a bad grade
2. **Emotion:** Stress
3. **Sensation:** Stomach upset
4. **Distress:** 7

Karate Chop or **KC**: **Even though** I am stressed because I might fail the exam, and my stomach is upset just thinking about it, **I completely accept myself**. (Repeat three times)

Tapping on the Thumb or **TH:** I am feeling stressed

Tapping on the Index Finger or **IF:** Because I have an exam coming up

Tapping on the Middle Finger or **MF:** I am really stressed because I might fail the exam

Tapping on the Little Finder or **LF:** My stomach is upset thinking about the exam

Tapping or rubbing the Gamut Point or **GP:** This stress

Tapping on the Karate Chop or **KC:** All this stress because I might fail the exam is making my stomach upset

Throughout the book we will be using the **Basic Recipe** in the sample scripts. Know that you can always use the **Hand Points** if you prefer, especially if you are in public and need to tap without others noticing.

As You Get Going

The Table of Contents is the best place to start in order to find a script relating to a situation you are facing. Scroll through the sections and see what topics call to you. However, don't feel that you have to use the book in any particular order. Keep in mind that there may be scripts in other sections that better apply to your situation. The scripts in each section are samples, filled and ready for tapping, but they do not represent all the various tapping subjects you might choose. Below each script in the book are lists of **Optional Because** or trigger issues and **Optional Emotions**. These suggestions, which relate to the topic covered in the sample script, can be substituted into the filled-in script, or you can use your own wording. Remember that the more personal you make the tapping the more effective it will be. Do not forget to tune into any physical Sensations you might be experiencing and add those in as you tap.

Keep in mind that what you say isn't as important as tapping. Do not be discouraged because you "don't know what to say." Start tapping and your brain will fill in the blanks. Also, be sure to make your tapping specific to what is happening in your life. Adding details to your words helps to sort through the emotions and release them more fully. Another important point to remember is to continue until you feel a shift in the emotion, or the physical sensations, or both. Ideally, you want to tap until your distress level reaches zero. Finally, tap gently but with gusto and use tapping to rant, vent, really spill out your emotions. Use the language that feels right to you; swearing is great to move your emotions, if you are comfortable with it. If you are alone, say the words with emphasis and if you are angry, don't be afraid to yell a little, being sure not to alert campus security.

Some of the sample scripts start with one set-up statement which you will repeat three times. Other scripts will feature three different set-up statements covering the same theme but written in a slightly different way. Note that you can create your set-up statement as one unchanging phrase or vary it; either way works. The set-up statements are a stream of consciousness form of writing and speaking. Do not worry about grammar when you tap. Be sure to start with the negative expression of emotions, to clear it and relax the fight or flight response, and add in a statement of acceptance.

If an event from earlier in your life surfaces while you are tapping, tap on it. It came up for a reason and is important. Don't hesitate to contact a practitioner or a professional if you are struggling.

In a few of the scripts throughout the book we have introduced the idea of ending a tapping session with a round of more positive statements. This positive tapping is not necessary and is not even part of the basic EFT formula. If, however, you want to try adding in some affirmative statements it is important to remember that you don't want to add positive statements until you have successfully reduced your level of distress to a 2 or below. Also, remember that you do not ever have to add the positive statements. EFT effectively clears the negative emotions that keep you stuck and stressed, automatically opening the way for brighter, positive emotions.

Section One
Classes and Homework

Classes, homework and professors are an inevitable part of college. Every semester requires new class choices and making the correct choices can be stressful. Added to that, the classes you take become more difficult as you begin to fulfill the requirements to complete your major. Daily homework assignments, papers that are due, group assignments, presentations, and examinations all add to the stress of your life on campus. Mix in the professors who create the syllabus and expect you to complete the work assigned, and you have a recipe for tension.

Tap out your feelings with EFT so you can more easily choose your classes, tackle homework and work with your professors. EFT can help to calm your nerves, settle your stomach, and clear the fog of stress that has covered your brain and made thinking all but impossible.

How Do I Choose Classes?

Choosing classes is challenging because, while many classes may look interesting, you know that you cannot take them all. You have to make strategic choices to fulfill the requirements necessary to graduate, which is your ultimate goal. It's harder to make good choices when you are stressed. Try this script to help you alleviate that stress so you can make clear decisions. Start with a deep breath and then assess and note your distress level and any physical sensations you may be feeling.

1. **Because:** There are so many classes to choose from and I don't know what classes to take...what if I make the wrong choices?
2. **Emotions**: Confusion and feeling overwhelmed
3. **Sensations:** Tightness in chest
4. **Distress:** 0-10 ________

The set-up phrase is worded in three ways. You may choose to say the script as written or you may choose your favorite version. Either way, be sure to say the set-up phrase three times.

KC: Even though I am so confused and overwhelmed because I don't know what classes to take, **I accept myself and how I feel.**

KC: Even though I am overwhelmed because there are so many classes to choose from and I don't even know what I want to study; my chest feels tight when I think about all of this, **I accept myself and how I feel**.

KC: Even though I am so confused and overwhelmed because I don't know what classes to take, my chest feels tight...how do I make this decision...how do I choose my classes, and what if I choose the wrong ones, **I accept myself and how I feel**.

EB: I am so confused
SE: There are so many classes to pick from
UE: And I have to pick the ones I am taking this semester
UN: What if I choose the wrong classes?
CP: I don't know what classes to take
CB: My chest feels tight just looking at all these choices
UA: So many to choose from

TH: What do I do?
EB: I am overwhelmed and confused
SE: I have to do this alone and that makes it even more confusing
UE: What if I choose the wrong classes?
UN: Make the wrong choices
CP: I don't even really know what I want to study in college
CB: This is so confusing, so overwhelming, I feel the tightness in my chest
UA: So confused, what classes do I pick
TH: This is overwhelming and so confusing

As before, continue tapping and add in whatever new words or ideas come to you as you go. Tap until you get to a distress level of 2 or below. And enjoy those classes!

Optional Because: My advisor is not helpful; I don't understand all the requirements I need to fulfill; The class descriptions are vague; I cannot get into a class because I have not fulfilled a prerequisite; The class I need is not offered this semester; The class I need is already full

Optional Emotions: Frustrated; Angry; Stressed-out; Worried; Tense

Classes are Hard

Classes are hard in college. You may have a class with lots of homework or one where you are expected to make a presentation. Plus, professors can be notoriously tough when it comes to grading. Take a look at the two scripts in this section which offer different options for tapping on classes. Be sure to check out the Optional Because and Optional Emotion sections for more suggestions. Choose which script best fits your situation and change what you need to make it your own. As always, start with a deep breath and take a moment to assess the level of your distress and note any physical sensations.

Homework is Harder Than I Thought It Would Be

1. **Because:** I have so much homework and it is harder than I thought it would be
2. **Emotions:** Stressed out and overwhelmed
3. **Sensations:** Upset stomach
4. **Distress:** 0-10 __________

KC: Even though I am so stressed out and overwhelmed because I have so much homework and it is harder than I thought it would be…just thinking about it upsets my stomach, **I accept myself and how I feel**. (repeat 3 times)

EB: I am stressed out
SE: I have so much homework to do
UE: So overwhelmed because it is harder than I thought it would be
UN: And there is so much of it that it stresses me out, upsets my stomach
CP: So much homework and it's so much harder than high school
CB: All this homework stresses me out and makes my stomach upset
UA: This homework is too hard, there is too much of it to do
TH: I am overwhelmed, stressed out, my stomach is upset

Continue tapping adding your words or following the script. See if you can bring your level of distress to a 2 or below. Take a deep breath as you finish and notice how you feel. Keep tapping if you need to and then, when you feel better, try adding the following script with more positive statements.

EB: I am feeling better
SE: Less stressed
UE: Less overwhelmed
UN: And I feel better about getting this homework done
CP: I am open to the idea that I can get this done, even though it seems impossible
CB: I am open to the idea that it isn't impossible to do all this work
UA: It feels good to release the stress
TH: To see that it is possible
EB: To get this work done
SE: And I choose to let this process be easy
UE: I choose to let it flow
UN: And I choose to get it all done to the best of my ability
CP: I choose to feel relaxed
CB: And get back to my homework
UA: To let it be easier than I thought it could be
TH: I choose to get it all done to the best of my ability

Optional Because: I don't understand what I am supposed to do; I am so busy all the time and there is never a break; I am not smart enough to do this homework; I am not good enough to do this; I can't handle all of this

There are more scripts in other sections of the book if you want to tap further on these issues. Check the Table of Contents for the corresponding page numbers.

Optional Emotions: Panicked; Frenzied; Stressed; Angry; Overwhelmed; Frustrated; Anxious; Stupid; Inadequate; Lacking confidence

Grading

Grades can take a toll on your psyche. You are likely concerned with your grades since how you perform in class is reflected in you GPA. Classes in your major may require that you maintain a particular grade point average. There are also scholarship requirements to be met, parents to satisfy, and the need to have the requisite grades for graduate school and job applications. All this adds to your stress. Use the following script to help reduce the stress surrounding grades. Tapping will allow you to get rid of the emotions that might be blocking you from success.

Start with a deep breath, tune into how you are feeling, and assess your distress level. Then begin to tap it out. If the words in the script do not reflect your situation, be sure to change them. You can use words you come up with or try some other options in the Optional Because and Optional Emotions sections below the script.

1. **Because:** The grading is so much different, so much harder this semester
2. **Emotions:** Stress, overwhelm and worry
3. **Sensations:** Tightness in my shoulders
4. **Distress:** 0-10 _______

KC: Even though I am so stressed out because the grading is so much different than last year, **I accept myself.**

KC: Even though I feel overwhelmed because it is so hard to get a good grade in this class, **I accept myself.**

KC: Even though I am worried because the grading is so tough and I feel tight in my shoulders, **I accept myself.**

EB: I am feeling overwhelmed because it is so hard to get a good grade
SE: This year is so much harder than last year
UE: How am I going to keep my grades up?
UN: All this worry is in my shoulders…they feel so tight
CP: All this worry about my grades
CB: This grading is so different…so much harder
UA: What if I fail something? My shoulders tighten up just thinking about it!
TH: I am so overwhelmed with worry about my grades
EB: I wonder if worrying makes it worse?
SE: I wonder if I will be just fine
UE: Other people can make good grades in these classes
UN: Why can't I?
CP: I'm open to releasing this overwhelming worry
CB: All this worry isn't helping me
UA: I'm so open to letting the worry go
TH: I'm open to releasing all this worry about my grades

Take a deep breath and release it. How are you feeling? Think about any physical feelings you have or if there is still a charge surrounding your grades. Continue tapping, adding your physical sensations and reasons why you feel you won't make good grades.

Optional Because: Studying for each class takes more time; I don't have time to study fully for each class; These classes matter more because they are about my major so they are more stressful; I can't afford to mess up now; I am having trouble managing my time

There are more scripts in other sections of the book if you want to tap further on these issues. Check the Table of Contents for the corresponding page numbers.

Optional Emotions: Afraid; Terrified; Angry; Doubtful; Dread; Frustration; Incompetent; Inept

I Don't Understand the Material

At some point during college you might find you don't understand the class material. This can be frustrating. Use this script to reduce the emotions you feel. By releasing these emotions, your brain is free to come up with a solution so you can get the information you need.

Begin by taking a deep breath and assessing your distress. Tune into your emotions and the physical sensations in your body.

1. **Because:** I don't understand the material, I have no idea what is going on in class
2. **Emotions:** Frustration and confusion; I feel stupid
3. **Sensations:** Pounding head
4. **Distress:** 0-10 _______

KC: Even though I have no idea what is going on in my class and it is so frustrating, **I accept myself.**

KC: Even though I am so confused because I just don't understand it all, and it makes my head pound, **I accept myself.**

KC: Even though I just don't get this and it stresses me out so much, **I accept myself.**

EB: I'm so confused
SE: I just don't understand this class
UE: What am I going to do?

UN: I'm so confused in this class
CP: I feel so stupid
CB: Why can't I understand this?
UA: I'm so confused
TH: I have no idea what is going on in this class
EB: My head is pounding from this confusion and frustration
SE: I'm falling behind because I just don't understand the material
UE: I'm going to end up failing this class because I just don't get it
UN: How do other people understand this?
CP: I wonder what I can do to help me understand?
CB: But I feel so stupid because I don't get it
UA: I wonder if I could find a way to understand?
TH: I'm open to figuring out a way to understand this class…

Stop and assess your level of distress. If it is still over a 3, continue to tap. Fill in with your own words, emotions and sensations. If the sensations move to different parts of your body, follow the sensation by substituting the new physical awareness as you tap. Once you have cleared the distressing emotions, you will discover that solutions come to you much more easily.

Optional Because: The professor does not explain the material well; The professor has an accent and is hard to understand

There are more scripts in other sections of the book if you want to tap further on these issues. Check the Table of Contents for the corresponding page numbers.

Optional Emotions: Anxious; Tense; Angry; Panicked

I Have So Much Homework

Homework and studying can become overwhelming, especially when something is due in every class. Below we've designed a general script that you can use to release the stress you're feeling around homework. If you want, add in the class that is worrying you or the specific homework or exam that you are concerned about. Being more specific is always best.

Take a deep breath in and a long breath out. Tune into how you are feeling about all the work you have to do for your classes. Focus on the emotions and body sensations that you feel. Rate the distress level and begin tapping.

1. **Because:** I have so much homework and I don't know how I'm going to get it all done (add in specific class or homework)
2. **Emotions:** Stress, feeling overwhelmed
3. **Sensation:** Tension in my neck, headache
4. **Distress:** 0-10 ______

KC: Even though I am stressed and overwhelmed because I have so much work to do, **I accept myself.**

KC: Even though I am so stressed because I have so much work to do and I have no idea how I'm going to get it all done...it's overwhelming, **I accept myself.**

KC: Even though I have so much work to do, I am so stressed out...my neck and head hurt, **I accept myself.**

EB: I have so much work to do
SE: I don't think I'll get it all done and I'm so stressed
UE: All this work *(specify class or homework)*
UN: I just can't keep up, it's overwhelming

CP: I'm never going to get it done on time
CB: All this homework and studying makes my neck and head hurt
UA: How do other people get it all done?
TH: All this work...*(specify class or homework)*
EB: How in the world will this apply in real life?
SE: I'm so stressed, I just can't do it all
UE: So much homework
UN: What if I fail?
CP: What if I do it all wrong?
CB: What if I work so hard and still get a bad grade?
UA: This sucks! My neck is so tight and I have a headache from all this stress...
TH: I'm never going to get through all this homework...

Take a deep breath in and a long breath out. Tune into the feeling and reassess your distress level. Let's try getting more specific and tune into where you feel the stress in your body. Again, add in your specific class, homework, exam or project.

EB: All this work...*(specify class or homework)*
SE: I feel the stress in my body
UE: I feel tension my neck
UN: All this stress and tension give me a headache
CP: I'm never going to get all this work done
CB: All this homework and studying for *(specify class or homework)*
UA: I just want to relax or hang out with my friends
TH: All this stress, I feel the tension in my body
EB: I feel tension in my neck and it's causing a headache
SE: All this work to do; I'll never get it done
UE: This sucks so much!
UN: My body is really feeling this stress

CP: I'm never going to get this work done *(specify class or homework)*
CB: And I won't get to hang out with my friends with all this work to do
UA: Sometimes I just hate college and all the work I have to do
TH: All this homework, I feel the stress in my neck and head

Take a deep breath and assess your level of distress. If it is higher than a 2 keep tapping through the script above. If it is lower, continue on.

EB: All this work
SE: I'm never going to get it all done
UE: How can I?
UN: I wonder how other people do it?
CP: Why can't I?
CB: I'll never get it done
UA: Other people do
TH: But I'll never get all this work done
EB: How do they do it?
SE: I wonder if I could too?
UE: No, I can't
UN: Yes, I can
CP: No, I can't
CB: Yes, I can
UA: Other people get it all done
TH: I'm open to getting this work done, calmly and clearly. I can do this, just like other people do...

Take a deep breath in and release slowly. Check if you have released the intensity surrounding your homework. You've done a great job. Keep tapping if you still have any residual distress or if it creeps back up again. Use this script as often as needed, replacing wording to suit your specific needs.

Optional Because: I have a paper due and I haven't even had time to start writing; I have to study for two upcoming exams; I have a board exam coming up; How am I supposed to read all the assignment when it is so long; All of my professors have assigned lots of homework at the same time

There are more scripts in other sections of the book if you want to tap further on these issues. Check the Table of Contents for the corresponding page numbers.

Other Possible Emotions: Frustrated; Hysterical; Desperate; Exhausted; Angry; Irritated; Burned out

Being Responsible

Studying is a big part of college. After all, you are there to learn, right? But what about the time after classes end? After you've spent all day or all week cracking the books, working hard. You deserve a break. You want to go out, hang with friends, party. Balancing your study life with your social life is difficult but important. Take a deep breath, tune into your emotions and the physical sensations you are experiencing and rate your distress level.

1. **Because:** I party too much…I need to be more responsible…I need to study but partying is more fun.
2. **Emotions:** Guilty, torn, and overwhelmed
3. **Sensations:** Exhausted
4. **Distress:** 0-10 _____

KC: Even though I am feeling guilty because I am partying too much, **I accept myself**.

KC: Even though I need to be more responsible, to study more, and I feel guilty and torn between partying and studying, I **accept myself**.

KC: Even though I feel guilty because I am not studying as much as I should be but I'd much rather party than study, **I accept myself.**

EB: I'm partying too much
SE: I just want to hang out...studying all the time is exhausting
UE: But I know I need to be more responsible...find a balance between studying and socializing
UN: I have so much work to do, but all I want to do is have fun with my friends
CP: I'm partying too much and I need to be more responsible
CB: Studying is no fun! I wish I could major in *fun*...that would be great
UA: I just need to study more and party less...I need to be more responsible
TH: That sounds so boring...ugh!
EB: I hate studying...I just want to hang out and have fun
SE: I feel guilty because I need to be more responsible, study more, find that balance
UE: It's really hard, though, because studying is so exhausting and really not fun
UN: I'm here to learn, so I need to find that balance and I feel guilty that I don't want to study
CP: I have so much work to do but I just want to socialize
CB: I'm open to finding a way to balance studying and fun
UA: I just want to hang out with my friends...
TH: I'm open to finding that happy balance between studying and socializing

Take a deep breath. Check your distress level. Can you add in any emotions to the above script? Keep adding and tapping until you lower the intensity. Once you do you will find the balance you need.

Optional Because: I watch too much television; I often skip class; I spend too much time ________ and don't get my homework finished; I have a new boyfriend/girlfriend and they take all my time; I am not motivated to study or go to class

There are more scripts in other sections of the book if you want to tap further on these issues. Check the Table of Contents for the corresponding page numbers.

Optional Emotions: Lethargic; Exhausted; Bored; Restless; Disinterested; Frustrated

Group Project

Here is an easy script to use if you have a group project that is causing you stress. Obviously, there are many aspects that could be causing this stress, but we picked some of the top stressors to use here. Substitute other emotions to meet your specific needs.

1. **Because:** Group project; everyone isn't pulling their weight and it could affect my grade
2. **Emotions:** stress, worry, frustration
3. **Sensation:** (Include if you feel any physical sensations related to your emotions)
4. **Distress:** 0-10 ______

KC: Even though I am so stressed out about this group project, **I accept myself.**

KC: Even though I am so stressed and worried about this project, because not everyone is pulling their weight and that is so frustrating, **I accept myself.**

KC: Even though I'm having issues, feeling stressed and frustrated because of this group project, and it could affect my grade, **I accept myself**.

- **EB:** This group project is so stressful!
- **SE:** This could really affect my grade in a bad way
- **UE:** I am so stressed, so worried because not everyone is pulling their weight
- **UN:** I am worried about this group project
- **CP:** It is so hard to work in a group, to get everyone to work together
- **CB:** We have to work together to get this done
- **UA:** It is so stressful
- **TH:** This could really impact my grade in a bad way and I am so stressed

Take a deep breath and assess your level of distress. Continue to tap, repeating this script, until your level of distress is a 2 or below.

Optional Because: We can't find a time that works for everyone; I can't stand working with one member of the group; One member of the group is taking over; One member of the group refuses to listen to anyone else; The group leader does not delegate at all; A member of the group is overbearing and obnoxious; No one listens to my ideas; Everyone else seems to know what they are doing and I don't

Optional Emotions: Irritated; Angry; Annoyed; Anxious; Overwhelmed; Ignored; Alone; Insecure; Insulted

Professor Problems

You cannot avoid professors in college. Hopefully, you like your professors and find them helpful and approachable, people you can go to if you have a question about their class. Occasionally, you may encounter a professor you do not like; one who frightens you, feels unapproachable, or does not communicate the material well. When you are feeling frustrated or downright mad at a professor, try tapping it out. We have provided two scripts with many optional choices at the end of script two. Be sure to add your own words to personalize the tapping to your situation.

I'm Afraid to Talk to My Professor

1. **Because**: I am afraid to talk to my professor and ask for help; she's mean and scary
2. **Emotion**: Fear, dislike even hate
3. **Sensation:** Clammy hands
4. **Distress:** 0-10 __________

KC: Even though I am afraid to talk to my professor (be specific about what professor/class) because she's mean and she scares me, **I accept myself and how I feel.**

KC: Even though I really hate my (insert class) professor because she's so mean and scary and she makes me feel stupid, **I accept myself and how I feel.**

KC: Even though I am scared to talk to my professor and I can't imagine going to office hours because she's so scary…it makes my hands clammy to think about, **I accept how I feel.**

EB: I don't like my professor
SE: She's so mean and scary
UE: Just being in her class is scary
UN: The thought of talking to her is even more frightening
CP: I hate my professor
CB: She talks down to the class

UA: Makes the whole class feel stupid
TH: I can't imagine going to office hours, talking to her alone
EB: I hate my professor
SE: She's so mean in class
UE: My hands get clammy even before I walk into class
UN: There is no way I want to go to her office after class to ask a question
CP: She's so mean in class, talks down to us, and makes me feel so stupid
CB: There's no way I can go to her office, alone; my hands feel clammy thinking about it
UA: I really hate this professor and how mean she is
TH: She's so scary, too scary to talk to, and she makes me feel so stupid

Take a deep breath and tune in to how you are feeling. What is your level of distress now? Do you feel a release? If not, repeat the tapping sequence, changing it as needed, until you feel relief from the emotions.

I Don't Like My Professor

Here is a second script about professors with different words used.

1. **Because:** My professor is arrogant and unapproachable
2. **Emotions:** Dislike, Anger
3. **Sensations:** Headache
4. **Distress:** 0-10 _______

KC: Even though I am feeling angry because my professor is arrogant and unapproachable, **I accept myself**.

KC: Even though I dislike my professor and I'm angry with him because he is arrogant and unapproachable, **I accept myself and my feelings**.

KC: Even though I'm feeling so angry with my professor because he is arrogant and unapproachable, **I accept myself**.

EB: My professor is arrogant and unapproachable
SE: I really don't like him
UE: How am I going to get through his class?
UN: I have such a problem with this professor
CP: He is arrogant in class
CB: So arrogant in class and I don't like him
UA: All this stress surrounding this professor
TH: I really don't like him
EB: He is arrogant and unapproachable
SE: All this anger
UE: I feel it in my body, I have a headache
UN: I get a headache every time I go to class
CP: He is so mean and arrogant
CB: Being in his class gives me a headache
UA: I am so angry at him…I really dislike my professor
TH: All this stress surrounding my professor

Optional Because: My professor never smiles; My professor seems to hate me; My professor hates the class; This professor has a reputation as unfriendly; No one likes this professor; I feel so stupid in this class; This professor's grading system sucks; The lecture class is so big and I'm a nobody, just a number to this professor; This professor's teaching style doesn't work with my learning style; I can't understand this professor because he/she has a heavy accent; This professor is a horrible teacher and can't communicate to the class

There are more scripts in other sections of the book if you want to tap further on these issues. Check the Table of Contents for the corresponding page numbers.

Optional Emotions: Fear; Afraid; Hesitant; Shy; Feeling stupid; Confused; Nervous; Irritated; Frustrated; Embarrassed; Lost; Tense; Shame; Terrified; Humiliated; Like I am an idiot

I Can't Decide on a Major

Some people go to college knowing exactly what they want to major in...others don't have any idea. Perhaps you are confused by all the requirements you need to complete your major. Try this general script when you are finding major decisions to be major distressing. As always, begin by taking a deep breath, determine what emotion you are feeling, rate your level of distress, and start tapping. Be sure to add, subtract, or substitute your own words to better encompass your emotions and any bodily sensations.

1. **Because:** I don't know what I want to major in but I have to decide very soon
2. **Emotions:** Stress and overwhelm
3. **Sensations:** (Include if you feel any physical sensations related to your emotions)
4. **Distress:** 0-10 __________

KC: Even though I am stressed and overwhelmed because I don't know what I want to major in, and I have to decide very soon, **I accept myself.**

KC: Even though this is really stressing me out, because I have no idea what I want to major in, **I accept myself.**

KC: Even though I am stressed out because I have no idea what I want to major in but I have to declare a major very soon, **I accept myself and these feelings.**

EB: All this stress and overwhelm
SE: I don't know what I want to major in
UE: I just don't know what to do
UN: What if I choose the wrong thing? What if I mess up?
CP: All this stress around my major
CB: I have to declare a major very soon but I don't know what I want to do
UA: I'm stressing so much about this
TH: What major do I declare?
EB: What should I do? I really don't know
SE: All this stress and overwhelm
UE: I have to declare a major and soon, but I don't know what to choose
UN: I hate not knowing what to do
CP: This stress isn't helping me
CB: All this stress because I don't know what to do
UA: All this stress about my major
TH: I am so overwhelmed trying to decide what major to choose

Take a deep breath in and a long breath out. Has this helped to lower your intensity rating? What is it now? Continue with this script making it as specific as possible, changing the wording as needed, and adding in any physical sensations you are experiencing, until your distress rating is a two or below.

Optional Because: I don't know what to pick for my major; I'm so confused, there are so many requirements for a major; There are so many requirements, how will I get it all done; How do I find an internship that works for my major; I chose a major, but I don't like it; I have a major, but I want to switch; What if it's too late to switch majors

Optional Emotions: Frustration; Confusion, Fear; Tension, Anxiousness

Required Versus General Ed Courses

Here is a script to use when you are struggling with the change from General Education classes to the upper level required courses you need for your particular major. Take a deep breath and tune into your feelings. Rate your distress and notice if you feel any physical sensations in your body.

1. **Because:** Changing from General Ed classes to the harder classes required for my major
2. **Emotions:** Stress; Struggle; Worry
3. **Sensations:** Upset stomach
4. **Distress:** 0-10 ______

KC: Even though I am struggling with the change from General Ed classes to the upper level courses I need for my major, **I accept myself and all these feelings**.

KC: Even though I am worried about moving to the harder, upper level courses, and I feel this stress in my body, **I accept myself**.

KC: Even though I have all these feelings, stress and worry, because I am switching from Gen Ed classes to more difficult upper level required classes, **I accept myself**.

EB: The classes are so different
SE: I have to do well in these classes because they are required for my major
UE: So much stress
UN: I feel it in my body…I'm nauseous

CP: All this stress about switching to required classes
CB: What if I don't do well?
UA: What if I fail?
TH: All this stress in my body about these required classes
EB: It's going to get so much harder now
SE: Now it's the real deal
UE: I feel it in my body...my stomach is upset
UN: The classes are so different
CP: This just adds to my stress
CB: All this stress about required classes; they are so much harder
UA: How am I going to do this?
TH: I feel this stress in my body, in my upset stomach...these required classes are so stressful

Take a deep breath and see if tapping has helped reduce your level of distress. If not, continue tapping and change the wording to suit your specific concerns.

Optional Because: I don't know if I like these classes; I should like these classes but I don't; These classes are for my major but I really hate them

Optional Emotions: Frustrated; Confused; Anxious; Overwhelmed; Apprehensive

Section Two
Grades and Exams

Many students worry about their overall GPA's and stress about getting straight A's. While this is noble, stress doesn't help you make those top grades. For new college students, it is important to remember that grading in college is not like grading in high school. Each professor will grade in his or her own way. What might have been A coursework for you in the past might now be considered B work. In fact, you might come to realize that the grade of B is quite an accomplishment in college.

No matter what your year of study, it's tough to change expectations, to give yourself a break, and to accept that all you can do is your best even if the letter you see on your transcript doesn't match your expectations. Tapping can ease your mind because it releases the stress, opening the door to a calmer you and better grades. The following scripts will help you tap in order to relax about grades in general as well as examinations and other presentations in particular. We've included two scripts at the end of this section using the Hand Points to help you release stress during an examination and a class presentation.

Worried About Grades

1. **Because:** I am worried about my grades…grading is so different from high school…I was a straight A student and now I'm not

2. **Emotion:** Worry/worried, Feeling stupid
3. **Sensations:** Tension and pain in neck
4. **Distress:** 0-10 ________

KC: Even though I am worried about my grades and I feel so stupid, because I was a straight A student in high school but I am not in college...grading is so different here, and this worry makes my neck tense and painful, **I accept myself and how I feel**. (repeat 3 times)

EB: I am worried about my grades
SE: I always got straight A's in high school but I don't in college
UE: I am a straight A student but not here and that worries me; it makes me feel stupid
UN: What is going on? How can it be so damn different?
CP: This grading sucks!
CB: I feel so stupid
UA: I was always a straight A student...what if I'm not really that smart?
TH: I feel so stupid now in college and I'm worried about my grades
EB: I'm so worried about my grades
SE: So scared that I'm stupid, not good enough
UE: Worried that I can't handle college
UN: I feel this worry in my neck, it hurts so much
CP: I am worried about my grades...if I can handle college
CB: I feel so worried...so stupid...what if I can't do this?
UA: All this worry, all this pain and tension in my neck
TH: Worried I won't do well in college...what if I can't handle it all

Take a deep breath and assess your level of distress. Continue to tap, repeating this script, until your level of distress is a 2 or below.

Optional Because: They give too much homework; I would do fine if they lightened up; How could anyone expect good grades with all that I have to do; I'm failing a class; I'm not smart enough; This is a waste of time; I took on too much

There are more scripts in other sections of the book if you want to tap further on these issues. Check the Table of Contents for the corresponding page numbers.

Optional Emotions: Frustration; Anger; Stress; Overwhelmed; Exhaustion; Incapable; Inadequate; Ashamed; Disheartened; Anxious

I Have a Failing Grade

If you received a failing grade on an assignment, exam or in a class, use this script to tap out your emotions. Begin with a deep breath in and a long breath out. Tune into all the feelings, and physical sensations you have about your failing grade. Can you pinpoint what happened? Is there something you can change or manage differently the next time? Jot down a few notes and get ready to tap. You know that releasing the stress now can only help to increase your success the next time.

1. **Because:** I failed a class/exam/assignment
2. **Emotions:** Freaking out; Angry
3. **Sensations:** Queasy stomach
4. **Distress:** 0-10 ______

KC: Even though I failed this (test/paper/class) and I'm freaking out right now, **I accept myself**.

KC: Even though I am angry and freaking out because I totally screwed up and now I have a failing grade and my stomach is all queasy, **I accept myself**.

KC: Even though I'm so angry that I failed this (test/paper/class), **I still accept myself and my feelings**.

EB: I failed the *(test/paper/class)*
SE: I'm so angry…I am freaking out
UE: I can't believe I failed it
UN: What am I going to do?
CP: This is really going to screw up my grade
CB: I messed up and I'm so angry
UA: I failed and now my stomach is queasy
TH: I failed the *(paper/test/class)* and I'm so angry; I am freaking out
EB: What if I fail again?
SE: I'm so worried about my grades and I feel it in my stomach
UE: This is going to mess up my grade and I am so angry!
UN: I can't believe I screwed up
CP: I failed and I am freaking out
CB: I'm so angry with myself!
UA: What if this happens again? My grades are going to suck
TH: I failed the *(test/paper/class)* and I am so angry…so freaked out

Take a deep breath in and a long breath out. Tune into how you are feeling. Check what your distress level is now. Keep tapping until your distress level is at a 2 or below.

Optional Because: I got a failing grade on my thesis; I failed again and that is bad; I have failed several classes; I might fail out of college

Optional Emotions: Feeling afraid; Terrified; Stupid; Anxious; Like a failure; Ashamed; Discouraged; Frustrated; Upset; Despairing; Worthless; Incompetent; Pathetic

GPA's and Straight A's

If you are worried about getting straight A's and concerns about your overall GPA keep you awake at night, use this script to release your stress. Tune in to your feelings, rate your level of distress and notice if you feel any physical sensations related to your emotions. Take a deep breath and begin tapping. Remember to use your own words to fit your exact situation where you need to.

1. **Because:** My GPA and getting straight A's
2. **Emotions:** Worry, stress
3. **Sensations:** Tightness in my chest, shortness of breath
4. **Distress:** 0-10 ______

KC: Even though I am worried about my GPA and getting straight A's and I can't get a good breath in when I think about it, **I accept myself**.

KC: Even though, I am stressed and worried about my GPA and getting A's and I feel tightness in my chest, I **accept myself and these feelings**.

KC: Even though I know I'm not helping the situation by worrying so much about getting straight A's and having a high GPA, it still stresses me out and I can't get a good breath in, **I accept myself and my worries**.

EB: I get so worried and stressed about making straight A's
SE: I worry all the time about my grades affecting my GPA
UE: I feel it in my chest, all this worry and stress
UN: I know this stress makes things worse
CP: I get so worked up and it affects my grades, my learning, my health
CB: I can't perform well when I am so stressed out about my grades and GPA

UA: Sometimes I wish I didn't care so much

TH: But if I don't worry then I might end up getting bad grades

EB: What if worry is making it harder to get good grades?

SE: What if worry is using energy that could go towards studying and getting A's like I want to?

UE: I know worrying isn't good for me

UN: I feel this worry in my chest…I can't take a deep breath

CP: I wonder if I can release this worry about my GPA and getting straight A's?

CB: I'm open to releasing this worry and stress surrounding my grades

UA: It would be so much healthier for me…I'd be able to breathe easier

TH: I'm open and ready to release this worry about my grades and my GPA. I'm open to releasing the stress and having more energy for success in my studies

Close your eyes, take a deep inhale and slowly exhale. Think about your grades and GPA. What is your distress level after tapping? Has it changed? If you find your intensity increasing, continue tapping on whatever emotions surface. Once your intensity drops to a 2, tap through all the points repeating the last line in this script at each point.

Optional Because: I am struggling with my GPA; There is no way I can raise my GPA; I am failing a class and it will ruin my GPA; My parents expect me to have a certain GPA; I need a particular GPA to get into (graduate school/law school/medical school or other); My GPA is lower than it was in high school and I study more; I can't do this – it's too hard; I took on too many classes

There are more scripts in other sections of the book if you want to tap further on these issues. Check the Table of Contents for the corresponding page numbers.

Optional Emotions: Afraid; Panicked; Tense; Frustrated; Angry; Desperate; Stupid; Ashamed

Too Much

College is busy and stressful. Stress causes the release of cortisol and cortisol muddles your brain. This makes studying and completing your work more difficult.[14] EFT helps to relax and dissipate the cortisol, clearing your brain so you can think better. Tap it out to reduce your stress. This is time well spent because it actually buys you more time. Once you relax, the entire studying process is much easier. Tap, relax, refocus and good luck.

1. **Because:** I have too much studying to do…I can't get it done…My grades might suffer
2. **Emotions:** Stressed and exhausted
3. **Sensation:** Can't sleep
4. **Distress:** 0-10___________

KC: Even though I am stressed and exhausted because I have too much studying to do…I can't sleep because I'm so stressed, **I accept myself and how I feel.**

KC: Even though I have all of this stress because I have so much studying to do…I am worried that I can't get it all done and my grades will suffer, **I accept myself and how I feel.**

KC: Even though I am stressed and exhausted because I have too much studying to do and if I don't get it done my grades might suffer, **I accept myself and how I feel.**

EB: I have so much studying to do
SE: Every professor gives homework
UE: And it is all due at the same time
UN: I have so much to do and I'm not sure I can get it all done
CP: I'm stressed and exhausted
CB: Just trying to keep up…to get it all done
UA: With all this stress I can't sleep
TH: I have to get it all done or my grades might suffer
EB: All this stress because of all the studying I have to do
SE: I'm so stressed I can't sleep
UE: I'm stressed, exhausted, worried about my grades
UN: Why do all of my professors give so much homework?
CP: I'm so stressed out I can't even sleep
CB: Exhausted, stressed and overworked
UA: I have to get it all done or I screw up my grades
TH: I'm so damn stressed out and exhausted because of all this studying

Take a deep breath and assess your level of distress. Continue to tap, repeating this script, until your level of distress is a 2 or below.

Optional Because: My classes are so hard; I have a paper due tomorrow and I haven't even started; I am behind in my studies; I had to miss class and now I am behind; I have too many things due at once; I'm not smart enough; College is too hard; I wish I wasn't at college

There are more scripts in other sections of the book if you want to tap further on these issues. Check the Table of Contents for the corresponding page numbers.

Optional Emotions: Overwhelmed; Nervous; Feeling anxious; Lack of confidence; Stupid; Not good enough; Dread

Studying for Examinations

If you experience stress when it comes to tests, you're not alone. The American Test Anxieties Association suggests that sixteen to twenty percent of students in the US have high test anxiety, with an additional eighteen percent experiencing moderately high test anxiety.[15] While we can't diagnose whether you have test anxiety, we can help you manage nervousness and worry surrounding tests. Use the following scripts to help you during the preparation and taking of exams.

Start by taking a deep breath and rating the intensity of your emotions. Change any words in the script to fit your situation. Be specific about your exam including the class or the subject you are studying. Tune into any physical sensations in your body. You will find more success once you have released the worry that is cluttering your brain.

1. **Because:** I have a big exam coming up...what if I forget everything?
2. **Emotions:** Nervous, worried and stressed
3. **Sensation:** Nauseous
4. **Distress:** 0-10 ________

KC: Even though I am stressed because I have a big exam coming up and I am afraid I will forget all that I've learned...the stress is making me nauseous, **I accept myself and how I feel.**

KC: Even though I feel stressed and worried about forgetting everything when I take the exam even though I studied, and it makes me nauseous thinking about it, **I accept myself**.

KC: Even though I feel nervous and stressed because this always happens to me...no matter how hard I study I know I will forget everything when I'm taking the exam…and it is so frustrating, **I accept myself**.

EB: I am so stressed out
SE: I have this big exam coming up soon
UE: And I feel so stressed about it that I'm nauseous
UN: What if I forget everything I've learned?
CP: What if I forget everything I've studied?
CB: It is all gone, slips away, and I draw a complete blank
UA: I feel so nauseous, so stressed out, over this big exam
TH: So nauseous and so stressed that I'll forget everything, screw it up
EB: I don't do well on tests, no matter how much I study
SE: I know I'm going to forget everything I've studied
UE: Draw a total blank when I'm in that exam
UN: I feel awful, so nauseous, so stressed
CP: I'm going to forget everything
CB: It's all going to be gone, everything I studied
UA: I'm so stressed out
TH: So worried that I'll forget everything, screw it all up
EB: I'm so nervous about this exam
SE: I'm sure I will forget everything
UE: I don't do well on tests no matter how much I study
UN: I'm so nervous that I'm nauseous
CP: I'm worried about failing even though I have studied
CB: This stresses me out so much…just thinking about taking this test, I'm already nauseous
UA: I hate tests!
TH: I get so nervous when I have exams
EB: It happens every time, no matter how much I study
SE: What if I forget everything even though I have studied, am studying now?
UE: I wonder if I can let this nervousness go?

UN: I'm sure I'd do much better on the exam if I wasn't worrying
CP: But I always get so worked up, I draw a blank
CB: I'm open to letting this stress go
UA: I'm open to trusting that I have studied and that I'm ready for this test
TH: I'm open and ready to release this stress about the exam, to trust that I have studied and am ready for this test so that I can allow myself to be successful...

Continue tapping until you feel a release of the stress or other emotion you've identified. Be sure to check in with your body by taking a deep breath and noticing how you feel. Once your intensity drops to a 2, tap through all the points repeating the last line in this script at each point. Come back to this script anytime you have a big exam to prepare for.

Optional Because: I will never be able to remember everything; I freeze up when I am taking exams; I am not a good exam taker; What if I study the wrong stuff; What if I don't study enough; I need to get a good grade; What if I fail

Optional Emotions: Afraid; Doomed; Blocked; Terrified; Paralyzed

Stress During Exams Using the Hand Points

At the beginning of the book in the How to Tap section we introduced the Hand Points. This script is specifically formulated for use with the hand points, which you will find on page 21 and in Appendix A. Hand Tapping offers similar results to tapping on the points of the Basic Recipe but in an inconspicuous way. If you find your stress level increasing during the exam, you can use the Hand Points to tap out your stress. Use the diagram on page 21 as a guide and **think** the words in your head, since you obviously can't talk out loud during the exam.

1. **Because:** Looking at the exam and drawing a blank
2. **Emotions:** Panicked, nervous, and stressed
3. **Sensations:** Racing heart
4. **Distress:** 0-10 ______

KC: Even though I'm getting stressed out just looking at this test and my heart is racing, **I accept myself**.

KC: Even though I'm sitting here at the exam completely panicked and now I can't remember anything, **I accept myself**.

KC: Even though I am panicking because I can't remember anything that I studied and this always happens to me when I take an exam, **I accept myself**.

TH: I'm panicking about this exam
IF: I'm sure I've forgotten everything I studied
MF: I'm going to fail
LF: This happens every freaking time I take an exam
GP: All this stress about this test...it gets me every time
TH: I can't remember anything...my mind is blank
IF: What if I studied the wrong material?
MF: I'm completely panicked and my heart is racing
LF: I'm going to fail this test
GP: I get so nervous about exams...I just go blank
KC: I get so stressed about exams and I end up forgetting everything

Take a deep breath and let it out. See how you feel. Is the stress showing up in your body? Try tapping through the hand points while you think about your physical feelings. Continue tapping until you have reduced your distress. Add in specifics from the test that have you particularly bothered or stumped. You can also continue to rub or tap on the Gamut Point to increase relaxation.

Optional Because: I studied the wrong material; I can't finish this test in time; This always happens; I am an idiot; What is wrong with me; I am going to fail this exam and this class

There are more scripts in other sections of the book if you want to tap further on these issues. Check the Table of Contents for the corresponding page numbers.

Optional Emotions: Despair; Doubt; Insecurity; Stupid; Shame; Terror

Presentations

Presentations may be part of your class grade. Speaking to a group can be nerve wracking. Knowing your material is a must, but good preparation does not always eliminate anxiety. Calming your nerves before your talk can help you to ace your presentation, and tapping can help with this. The following script will help to ease your nerves while you prepare your presentation.

1. **Because:** I have a presentation coming up…what if I forget everything
2. **Emotion:** Nervous, scared, worried
3. **Sensation:** Butterflies in stomach
4. **Distress:** 0-10 _______

KC: Even though I am so nervous because I have a presentation coming up and I'm worried I'll forget everything as soon as I stand up to talk, **I accept myself and all these feelings.**

KC: Even though I have butterflies in my stomach because of this presentation I have to do, **I accept myself.**

KC: Even though I am so nervous and worried about this presentation, and I'm scared I'll forget everything, **I accept myself.**

EB: This presentation is making me nervous
SE: All this worry about this presentation
UE: I have butterflies in my stomach just thinking about it
UN: What if I forget everything?
CP: I'm so nervous…I feel it in my stomach
CB: I'm nervous and scared about this presentation
UA: So scared I'll forget everything
TH: I have butterflies in my stomach
EB: All this worry about this presentation
SE: Presentations make me so nervous
UE: What if I forget everything and make a fool out of myself?
UN: I'm so nervous
CP: I feel it in my stomach, just thinking about it
CB: I'm open to releasing these nerves, this fear
UA: All this worry and fear about the presentation
TH: I'm open to releasing these feelings and having a successful presentation

Continue repeating this script until your distress level lowers. At that point, you may find doing a round or two of the points while saying the last line of this script will add positive motivation for a successful presentation.

Optional Because: I've never done a presentation before; This presentation is a huge part of my grade - I don't want to mess up; People will laugh at me; I'll get a bad grade on my presentation; I'm not ready for this presentation; Everyone else will do better than me; I have an upcoming performance; I might forget my lines; I have an upcoming concert; I might forget the music; I might forget my part or miss my cue

There are more scripts in other sections of the book if you want to tap further on these issues. Check the Table of Contents for the corresponding page numbers.

Optional Emotions: Embarrassed; Terrified; Panicked; Anxious; Unsure; Not good enough

Tapping on Presentations Using the Hand Points

Take a look at the next script using the hand points, found on page 21 and in Appendix A. As with examinations, you cannot tap on the Basic Recipe during a presentation. You may, however, use the hand points before you start your presentation to soothe any stress you are feeling.

1. **Because:** I am about to begin my presentation and I cannot remember a thing
2. **Emotion:** Paralyzed with fear
3. **Sensation:** Nauseous
4. **Distress:** 0-10 ________

KC: Even though I am paralyzed with fear and nauseous because I cannot remember a word of my presentation which is about to begin…there is no way I can stand up and do this, I **accept myself.** (repeat 3 times)

TH: My presentation is about to begin and I've drawn a blank
IF: I can't remember a word that I'm supposed to say
MF: I'm paralyzed with fear and so nauseous
LF: There's no way I can get up there and speak

GP: I'm paralyzed with fear…I don't think I can even move
KC: I've forgotten it all, drawn a blank, going to totally screw this up

Take a breath and assess your level of distress. Has the level dropped to a 2 or below? Are your emotions showing up as body sensations? Continue tapping until your distress level drops. You can rub or tap on the Gamut Point to increase relaxation.

Optional Because: The play is about to begin and I cannot remember my lines; The concert is about to start and I have forgotten the music/my part; Everyone is going to be staring at me; I have to go on soon and I might miss my cue; I have to start but I don't feel well

There are more scripts in other sections of the book if you want to tap further on these issues. Check the Table of Contents for the corresponding page numbers.

Optional Emotions: Afraid; Terrified; Nervous; Worried; Tense; Sick; Full of dread

Section Three
Time Management

College is a juggling act. Between classes, social obligations and finding time to sleep, it often feels impossible to manage it all. College requires an entirely new level of responsibility and that responsibility starts from your first step onto campus. So how do you handle it all? How can you be social and get good grades? How can you stay motivated to get it all done? How can you negotiate delicate relationship issues with new friends and with professors? All without going crazy? Well, we have some tapping scripts that we think will help. Go ahead, dive in. It may seem like you don't have time for one more thing, but EFT has a way of giving you more time by evaporating stress and worry. Tapping out your feelings allows you to succeed in school and have more time to enjoy your university experience.

I Don't Know How to Organize

When you have too much to do and no idea how to get it all done, try this script. Take a deep breath and exhale, releasing some tension. Now pay attention to your emotions. Do you notice any physical sensations accompanying the emotions you are feeling? Determine your distress level and start tapping.

1. **Because:** I don't know how to organize it all, my classes, my homework, my friends
2. **Emotions:** Overwhelmed and stressed

3. **Sensation:** Headache
4. **Distress:** 0-10 ________

KC: Even though I am feeling stressed and overwhelmed because I have too much to do and I don't know how to organize it all, plus I have a headache from all the stress, **I accept myself and my feelings**. (repeat 3 times)

EB: I'm overwhelmed
SE: There's so much to do between classes, homework, friends to hang out with
UE: And I have no idea how to organize it all, how to do everything
UN: I'm behind with everything and there's no way I can catch up
CP: I'm totally overwhelmed and stressed
CB: All this stress and overwhelm gives me a headache
UA: I don't even have time to sleep
TH: I have too much to do, too much homework, there's no way I can get it all done
EB: There are friends to see, social obligations that I want to be a part of
SE: But I don't have time
UE: There are classes and homework
UN: There's so much to do and never enough time to get it all finished
CP: I can't organize all of it, get it all done, and sleep
CB: I am exhausted with all of this and it makes my head hurt
UA: Feeling overwhelmed, stressed and exhausted
TH: There's too much to do

As you end, take another deep breath. How do you feel? Did any new thoughts or emotions surface as you tapped? Add those into your tapping and continue until your level of distress falls to a 2 or below.

Optional Because: I have no time to make friends; I have no time to socialize with my friends; I have so much homework and I can't do anything else; It feels like no one else has to do as much as I do; I have to balance a job with school; I have no time to sleep

There are more scripts in other sections of the book if you want to tap further on these issues. Check the Table of Contents for the corresponding page numbers.

Optional Emotions: Lonely; Disconnected; Alone; Sad; Anxious; Angry; Panicked; Nervous; Tense; Afraid; Uptight; Edgy; Upset; Frustrated; Suffering

I Don't Have Time For a Break

In college, your attention is centered around studying and classes. Taking time off to relax is difficult. After a while, you become exhausted. You need a break. This script helps you tap through the stress of having too much to do and not enough time for you. Add any other wording that feels better to you. Start with a deep inhale and a long exhale. What emotions are you feeling? Assess your level of distress and then start tapping.

1. **Because:** I have so much to do and not enough time…do I study or party?
2. **Emotion**: Stressed and overwhelmed
3. **Sensation:** Tight shoulders and neck
4. **Distress:** 0-10 _________

KC: Even though I am stressed because of all that I have to do…I don't know if I can do it all, and the stress is making my shoulders and neck tight, like knots, **I accept myself.**

KC: Even though I'm feeling stressed because there is so much to do and not enough time…I'm trying to balance my social life with my class workload, and I feel overloaded and overwhelmed…I don't know how to decide what to do, how to do it all, **I accept myself and all these feelings**.

KC: Even though I am overwhelmed with all the work and all the social obligations at college, and I feel so much stress as I try to balance everything…the stress is in my shoulders and neck, **I accept myself and how I feel.**

EB: I'm overwhelmed and overloaded
SE: There's so much I have to do and I feel the stress in my neck and shoulders
UE: So much homework that I have to get done
UN: But I really want to go out with my friends
CP: There are so many parties to go to
CB: I want to see my friends but how can I do it all
UA: School is so overwhelming that I really need a break
TH: But I don't really have time to take a break
EB: I hate all this stress and overwhelm…I feel it in my neck and shoulders
SE: So many assignments to get done
UE: I have a paper due, a project coming up, and an exam in a week
UN: Already I have no time
CP: I really want to go out and see my friends
CB: I'm so overwhelmed. How do I juggle it all?
UA: What do I do?
TH: I really need to study
EB: I really need a break, too
SE: I could go out every night, hang out with my friends
UE: But then my grades would suffer
UN: My grades might slip

CP: So much to do, so many decisions
CB: Either way I'm screwed
UA: I want to do both
TH: Feeling so overwhelmed and overloaded

Continue to tap until your distress level has dropped to a 2 or lower. Now try tapping on the points again but this time add in some positive suggestions to help you decide how to balance your time and feel good about that decision. You don't need to start at the Karate Chop point this time around. Just tap the basic recipe points, as follows.

EB: I'm so stressed about this decision
SE: I want to go out tonight but I have so many deadlines
UE: Is there any way I can get everything done that needs doing today...
UN: So that I can go out tonight
CP: How can I make this decision?
CB: Is there a clear answer?
UA: Maybe there isn't a clear answer
TH: Maybe I can study now and go out for a bit later
EB: Is that possible, can I do both?
SE: Or is that too much?
UE: What is my body telling me...what answer is popping into my head?
UN: How can I be sure of the answer?
CP: Maybe it's okay to do both
CB: Maybe it's Not okay to do both
UA: Maybe I really need to study tonight and go out tomorrow
TH: Or maybe I can go out for a little while tonight
EB: After all, I can only study for so long
SE: But I do have so much to do
UE: I ought to go to bed and sleep if I don't study
UN: I may go out for a while

CP: I may stay in and study
CB: I may decide to go to bed early and go out tomorrow night
UA: Either way I accept myself and my decision
TH: Whatever I decide, I can make the best choice for me in this moment and at this time

Whatever you decide, taking time to de-stress so you can make a clear choice is important. From that relaxed place inside you can begin to find your own balance and make your best decisions.

Optional Because: I don't have any time; I need time for me; I never get to sleep; I don't have time to exercise; I don't have time to go out to dinner; I don't have time to talk to my friends or family on the phone; I need a nap; Other people go out and seem to make it work; I never get to hang out with my friends; I haven't made any friends to hang out with; It's hard to meet fun, quality people to socialize with when I am so busy; I cannot handle any more; It feels like all of the work comes at once and then there is too much to do; I might lose my scholarship; I just don't care anymore

There are more scripts in other sections of the book if you want to tap further on these issues. Check the Table of Contents for the corresponding page numbers.

Optional Emotions: Frustration; Tension; Anger; Irritation; Envy; Fear; Isolation; Exhaustion; Unmotivated; Ambivalent

Procrastination

Procrastination is a one of the most insidious forms of resistance. Most of us have procrastinated, waited too long to get something started or finished. Procrastination leaves us feeling stressed out, overwhelmed with extra work we've made for ourselves – because professors are always giving more homework whether we've finished an earlier assignment or not – sometimes angry at ourselves or even a little ashamed that we weren't more proactive. Below are three tapping scripts to help you overcome any procrastination. As you tap out the resistance you are feeling, you might discover that what you need to do won't be as bad as you imagined.

I Don't Want to Do This

There are many reasons people put off getting something done. An assignment may feel too hard and that can be scary. If you don't like a class or a professor, doing the work he or she assigns may not be a high priority. Outside influences can tempt you to put off your work, like that series you binge-watched, or that nap that ate away all your time to study. And, of course, in college there are a few social engagements that might provide a distraction from the books. Give this script a try if you find that you don't even want to get started on whatever it is you need to accomplish. Take a deep breath, assess your emotions around the specific issue and rate your level of distress. It's time to start tapping.

1. **Because**: I have a paper to write and I don't want to do it…I want to watch shows
2. **Emotion:** Paralyzed
3. **Sensations**: Sleepy, heavy, weighted down
4. **Distress**: 0-10 ______________

KC: Even though I'm paralyzed because I have a big paper to write and I don't know where to start, so I am watching shows instead…I feel so heavy, weighted down with this paper…**I accept myself and my feelings**.

KC: Even though I'm paralyzed because of this paper and I really just want to watch shows…just thinking about writing this paper makes me sleepy, **I accept myself and my feelings**.

KC: Even though I'm paralyzed because I hate writing papers and I feel like I can't even move, can't get it done, my body feels so heavy and sleepy, and **I accept myself and my feelings**.

EB: I'm paralyzed
SE: I have to write this paper and I don't want to
UE: I hate writing papers
UN: I'm not good at writing papers and I don't know where to start
CP: Just thinking about it makes me feel sleepy and weighted down
CB: Writing papers really scares me…I feel paralyzed
UA: I'm sleepy…I'd rather take a nap
TH: It's going to take so long to write this stupid paper
EB: I have to do research, figure out citations
SE: I hate writing papers, I'm not that good at it
UE: And this is going to take a long time
UN: Thinking about this paper makes me sleepy…I really want to take a break…watch shows
CP: I don't want to write this paper…I feel really tired… weighted down by all this pressure
CB: It's so stupid anyway…why do we have to write papers?
UA: All this researching and writing is going to take such a long time
TH: All of it, the writing, research, all of it really paralyzes me

Keep tapping until you feel better, then do a check in. How are you feeling? Are you feeling any new emotions or physical sensations? Add in whatever is present for you and tap until you bring down your level of distress.

Optional Because: I can't do another thing; It is all too much; I can't balance everything they want me to do so I just won't do it; I don't understand this assignment/test/paper; I have so much and I can't settle down to do any of it; Why do I need this class anyway; This class/paper/assignment is so boring; I want to go out with friends

There are more scripts in other sections of the book if you want to tap further on these issues. Check the Table of Contents for the corresponding page numbers.

Optional Emotions: Overwhelmed; Exhausted; Angry; Nervous; Panicked; Stressed; Frenzied; Defensive; Shut Down; Powerless; Bored

I've Done It Again...Put Off What I Have to Do

You've done it again, put off that assignment or paper that is worth 30% of your grade. You know you have to finish it and now you are running out of time. You almost wonder if you should start at all, but you know that not turning it in is not an option. Take a deep breath, tune into your emotions, determine your level of distress, and start tapping.

1. **Because:** I always procrastinate and I've done it again, put off studying for that exam...when will I learn
2. **Emotion:** Shame and anger at self
3. **Sensation:** (Include if you feel any physical sensations related to your emotions)
4. **Distress:** 0-10 ________

KC: Even though I'm ashamed and angry because I did it again, waited too long...I put off studying for that exam, and now I have so much to get done, **I accept myself and what I've done**.

KC: Even though I'm ashamed and angry because I always wait until I have to rush to get things done…now I'm in a bind because I have to study for this exam and do more homework, **I accept myself and what I have done**.

KC: Even though I'm so angry and ashamed because I did it again, I waited to study…now I have this major exam and I'm not prepared, **I accept myself and what I've done.**

EB: I'm ashamed of myself
SE: And I'm so damn angry at myself
UE: I did it again
UN: I procrastinated, waited too long
CP: I have this exam coming up and no time to study
CB: On top of the stupid exam I have more homework
UA: How did I let this happen, again?
TH: I'm so damn angry with myself
EB: I really screwed up
SE: I waited too long to study for this exam and now I don't know how to get it all done
UE: This exam is really important…all my homework is
UN: I'm so angry, so ashamed
CP: I do this all the time, procrastination, and I hate it
CB: This anger because I waited too long…procrastinated
UA: I'm ashamed of myself and so angry
TH: So angry, so ashamed…I totally screwed this up

Keep tapping until you feel calmer, more focused, ready to tackle the studying you need to accomplish. As you tap, use whatever words come up for you. Really make this your tapping, your rant, your time to vent. If you are in a private place, yell it out. Cuss it out. This is your tapping time so make it about you and how you feel so you can really let go of those emotions.

Optional Because: I am an idiot; I am going to fail; I will never get it all done now; Why did I do this; I don't know how to do this so I didn't; I hate myself and college; I messed up again and I always do this

There are more scripts in other sections of the book if you want to tap further on these issues. Check the Table of Contents for the corresponding page numbers.

Optional Emotions: Worry; Tension; Irritation; Frustration; Feeling Overwhelmed; Stressed; Overworked; Panicked; Pathetic

I Eat to Avoid my Work and Now I'm Gaining Weight

Eating can be a form of resistance. Those cravings for salt or sugar might be a sneaky way of resisting whatever it is that you don't want to do. Of course, there are many reasons for cravings so if you don't think this is your reason, look in Section Six, Physical and Emotional Health, for more ideas. If you recognize that when the studying gets tough you want ice cream or chips, and you make the effort to find and satisfy the craving rather than do homework, you might be using food to take you away from the realities of studying. Give the following script a try and, as always, substitute your own words or feelings to make it personal.

Weight is a very complex issue. Keep a journal of whatever comes to you as you tap. You might find that there is more to your cravings than simply avoiding homework. If so, tap on what you discover or, if this feels like too much to handle alone, contact an EFT practitioner or go to your school's counseling services for one-on-one help. Please go to Appendix C for more resources regarding weight and body issues.

1. **Because:** I eat cookies rather than studying and now I'm gaining weight
2. **Emotions:** Ashamed...I hate myself when I do this
3. **Sensations:** My body feels heavy and uncomfortable
4. **Distress:** 0-10 ________________

KC: Even though I am ashamed of myself, because I eat cookies rather than studying, and my body feels so heavy and uncomfortable, **I accept myself just as I am**.

KC: Even though I'm ashamed of myself because I eat cookies rather than study and now I am gaining weight, **I accept myself just as I am**.

KC: Even though I hate myself and I'm so ashamed because I am eating all these cookies rather than studying...I'm gaining weight, and my body is uncomfortable, **I accept myself and how I feel**.

EB: I'm so ashamed of myself
SE: I keep eating all these cookies
UE: Rather than studying, I go buy these damn cookies and eat them
UN: I eat and eat and eat, so many cookies
CP: I'm gaining weight and I feel uncomfortable
CB: I hate myself for doing this
UA: Why don't I just get my work done...Why do I keep eating?
TH: I can't stand myself when I do this, eat all this sugar, and I don't feel well
EB: My body feels uncomfortable
SE: I feel so ashamed...so heavy...and I know I'm gaining weight
UE: All these cookies, it's so much easier to eat them than to study

UN: There is so much studying to do that I don't even know where to start
CP: It's easier to eat cookies even when they make me feel bad
CB: So much stress at college
UA: All this stress…so much to do…I'd rather eat cookies
TH: Even though I am so ashamed of myself and I don't feel good when I do
EB: And I don't get my homework done
SE: So much stress
UE: These cookies make it better…numb the stress, even for a little bit
UN: So much stress, so much to do, all these cookies
CP: I am so ashamed of myself for eating these cookies
CB: I don't know how to stop
UA: All this stress weighs me down
TH: All this stress at college…I'm just eating cookies to numb it, avoid it and I feel so ashamed

Keep tapping you feel a shift in your emotions. If you feel new emotions arise as you tap, do a few tapping rounds and substitute in the new emotions. Continue to work with this script or one that suits your situation until you feel relief from the shame and the stress.

Optional Because: I use food, salty/sugary/fatty/fried/ to numb me because school is too hard; I use food to escape; I use food as an excuse to stop studying; Studying is so overwhelming that I eat instead; Food is my friend and is always there for me; I am smoking to avoid studying

There are more scripts in other sections of the book if you want to tap further on these issues. Check the Table of Contents for the corresponding page numbers.

Optional Emotions: Overwhelmed; Vulnerable; Sadness; Frenzied; Guilty; Out of Control; Afraid; Ugly; Anxious

Motivation

Sometimes you don't feel like doing something you know you have to do. You lack motivation. There are lots of reasons for lack of motivation. Going to class, especially if that class doesn't hold your interest, or is early in the morning, or is scheduled when your friends have a break, can wreak havoc on your inner dedication. Heck, you don't want to be there when you could be having coffee and a bagel with your buddies. Use this script to help you break through your motivational slump and inspire you to get to class. Begin by taking a deep breath and assessing your emotions and sensations surrounding your class or classes.

1. **Because:** I can't get motivated to go to class
2. **Emotions:** Bored and annoyed
3. **Sensations:** Heavy, tired, and sluggish
4. **Distress:** 0-10 ______

KC: Even though I can't get motivated to go to class, because I am bored and annoyed with the class and I just want to hang out with my friends, **I accept myself**.

KC: Even though I don't want to go to class, and I feel so sluggish right now thinking about it, **I accept myself and the fact that classes are a part of college**.

KC: Even though I know I have to go to class and that's so annoying, because I am not motivated to go, I really don't want to go to class, I **accept myself and these feelings**.

EB: I don't want to go to class

SE: I just can't get motivated to go…I feel so heavy and sluggish
UE: I can't stand this class, it's so boring
UN: I'm never going to use this information
CP: Why do I have to take this stupid class? I'm so annoyed
CB: Seriously, how will this apply in "real life"?
UA: I want to skip class today
TH: I feel so unmotivated…I'd rather hang out with my friends
EB: I don't want to go
SE: I could be doing something else…something fun
UE: I could be sleeping
UN: I just don't want to go to class…it's so boring
CP: I don't want to go.
CB: Maybe it won't be so bad
UA: But I really don't want to go
TH: I wish I could skip today…I just don't want to go to class
EB: I'm not going to go to class
SE: I am going to go to class
UE: I'm not going to class…it's so boring
UN: I am going to class
CP: No, I'm not going
CB: Yes, I am going
UA: I'm not going to class today
TH: I am going to class today

Take a nice deep breath in and reassess your distress level. Keep tapping if you need to, making sure to add wording that makes the situation true to you.

Optional Because: This class is boring; I need to sleep/want to take a nap; I would rather relax; I want to watch television; I need to run errands; My friends are all going out; I am burned out with all my classes; I will never use this class in real life; This class is too hard; This class is too easy; I am failing this class so what's the point; The professor hates me; I hate the professor

There are more scripts in other sections of the book if you want to tap further on these issues. Check the Table of Contents for the corresponding page numbers.

Optional Emotions: Irritated; Frustrated; Uninterested; Exhausted; Burned out; Weary; Resistant; Nervous; Angry

Managing School and Other Commitments

Having trouble managing your time? It can certainly be a juggling act in college, even for the best time managers. It's a learned skill and chances are you're still trying to figure out how to get everything done. Try giving this tapping script a shot. It will help clear your mind so you will be able to constructively manage your precious time. Close your eyes and tune into the feelings you have surrounding time management. Use the distress scale to assess your intensity level.

1. **Because:** Managing time, school work plus other commitments
2. **Emotion:** Frustration, overwhelm
3. **Sensation:** Shoulder tightness
4. **Distress:** 0-10 _______

KC: Even though I am frustrated and overwhelmed because I have such difficulty managing my time, **I accept myself**.

KC: Even though I have school work plus other commitments, and I just can't figure out how to juggle it all…I'm feeling overwhelmed and the stress makes my shoulders feel tight, **I accept myself**.

KC: Even though I am so frustrated and overwhelmed because I can't seem to figure out how to get all my work done, **I accept myself and my feelings.**

EB: So much to juggle
SE: How do I get it all done?
UE: I am terrible at time management
UN: I can't figure it out
CP: I can't get it all done
CB: How do other people do it?
UA: I'm so bad at managing my time
TH: I'll never get everything done in time
EB: My shoulders are so tight, I'm so stressed and overwhelmed
SE: How am I supposed to get all this work done?
UE: When do I get to sleep?
UN: When do I get relax, and socialize?
CP: I'm so overloaded
CB: I'm so overwhelmed
UA: I wish I could manage my time better
TH: I'm so bad at time management
EB: My work seems to come in waves
SE: It's all or nothing
UE: It's so overwhelming! I feel it in my shoulders
UN: I have so much to do and I can't figure out how to get it all done
CP: I am terrible at managing my time
CB: My shoulders are so tight, holding all this frustration
UA: I'll never figure it out
TH: It's all so overwhelming!

Now take a deep breath and release it. Tune back in and assess your distress level. Has it lowered? Tap through the above script until you have lowered it to a 2. Then try the following continuation of the script, adding in specifics and some positive statements to your tapping.

EB: Time management is so frustrating
SE: How do I fit everything in?
UE: Not only do I have school work, but I also have other commitments
UN: And I need to sleep at some point
CP: This is so frustrating
CB: I hate having to manage my time
UA: This sucks!
TH: I wish I could easily get everything organized and done without all this stress
EB: How do other people do it…homework, exams, socializing
SE: My grades are affected because I can't manage my time
UN: I wish I could just crawl into bed and pull the covers over my head
CP: All this work plus other commitments leaves me no time for a social life
CB: I'm so overwhelmed and overloaded
UA: How do I get it all done and still have a life?
TH: How the heck do other people do this all?
EB: Sometimes I can't get my act together
SE: Sometimes I don't really care…it's too overwhelming
UE: But I really do care…I just wish I could manage my time better
UN: I wonder if I could learn to manage my time?
CP: Other people do it, maybe I can too?
CB: I'm open to finding a way to manage my time without getting stressed out
UA: I wonder if I can?
TH: I am open to finding a way to reduce my stress by managing my time well

Take a deep breath. Notice your level of distress after the tapping. You may want to tap and say the last line on each point in the Basic Recipe to end on a positive note. Often you may find that your stress level has lessened immediately after tapping and then, a few hours later, you'll realize that you *are* actually managing your time and getting things done! How great is that? Keep tapping as specifically as you can whenever you feel "time" breathing down your neck.

Optional Because: I have social commitments; I have job/work obligations; I am involved in athletics; I am involved with social organizations; I am volunteering

There are more scripts in other sections of the book if you want to tap further on these issues. Check the Table of Contents for the corresponding page numbers.

Optional Emotions: Upset; Angry; Afraid; Exhausted; Worried; Distressed; Frazzled

Balancing Job with School

If you are a student who is juggling work with school, you have avenues of stress that your friends might not understand. Here is a script and some other tapping ideas to help you relax and hopefully allow you to get more done while feeling less overwhelmed.

1. **Because:** I have to work, go to class, and study and I have no time for myself or my friends
2. **Emotions:** Burned out
3. **Sensations:** I have a headache
4. **Distress:** 0-10 ___________

KC: **Even though** I am burned out at college because I have to work and go to school, and I have no time to see friends, no time for myself, **I accept myself and how I feel**. (3 times)

EB: I am burned out
SE: I have to work and go to school
UE: I don't have time for myself
UN: I don't have time to see friends
CP: All I do is go to class, work and study
CB: I barely have time to sleep
UA: I am stressed, totally burned out
TH: I have too much to do...no time for me...no time for friends

The continuation of this script illustrates how you can expand your tapping to include other emotions or circumstances that fit your life and what you are experiencing. Also, see the **Optional Because** and **Optional Emotions** sections below for more ideas.

EB: It's so unfair
SE: None of my other friends have to work and go to school
UE: But I have to work and go to class and I don't have time for seeing friends
UN: I am so burned out
CP: It's not fair...
CB: I'm so stressed, so burned out, and my friends don't get it
UA: They don't have to work and go to school
TH: It's so unfair, all that I have to do, and I have no time for me

Optional Because: I have too much to do; My friends don't have this much; No one understands how much I have to get done; I am all alone in this; No one can help me

There are more scripts in other sections of the book if you want to tap further on these issues. Check the Table of Contents for the corresponding page numbers.

Optional Emotions: Frustration; Irritation; Unfair/it's not fair; Anger; Exhaustion/worn-out

Getting Around Campus

Many campuses are large and spread out. Often you will have back to back classes that are on opposite sides of campus, making getting to class on time difficult. Each semester you need to find a new routine to fit into a new schedule. Using this script can help you ease the stress and frustration as you navigate campus, so you can find a creative solution to make your scheduling issues work for you.

Take a deep breath and think about your issue. Identify the emotions you are feeling, rate your level of distress and start tapping.

1. **Because:** Campus is so big…I'm always late…and it changes each semester.
2. **Emotions:** Frustrated, stressed, and annoyed
3. **Sensations:** (Include if you feel any physical sensations related to your emotions)
4. **Distress:** 0-10 ______

KC: Even though I am frustrated and stressed because this campus is so big and I can never get to my classes on time, **I accept myself.**

KC: Even though I hate being late all the time and I get so stressed about it because campus is so big, **I accept myself.**

KC: Even though I am so frustrated because everything is so spread out on campus and my schedule changes every semester, which means I have to adjust yet again, **I accept myself and the situation**.

EB: This campus is so big and I am always running late…I hate it
SE: How do other people get to class on time?
UE: Why can't I do it? It's so overwhelming and stressful
UN: This is so frustrating and annoying
CP: Classes are so spread out! How am I supposed to get to class on time?
CB: I don't get how others do it
UA: I always end up being late and the professor gets annoyed
TH: I hate being late because the campus is so big
EB: I wonder how I can manage this?
SE: There must be a way…other people somehow manage to do it
UE: Why can't I?
UN: I'm open to finding a way to make this easier to manage
CP: I really can't stand always feeling rushed and late
CB: What can I do to make this easier on myself?
UA: This campus is so spread out. I'd have to have super powers to get everywhere on time
TH: But maybe I can figure out a way to make it work so I don't feel rushed and late all the time

Take a breath and check in with your distress level. Has it changed? Did any possible solutions come up for you? Simply tapping isn't going to make all your classes suddenly move to the same building but once the emotional block is released you'll be amazed at your ability to come up with creative solutions.

Optional Because: None of my classes are near to one another; I can't change my schedule so I am stuck; I have an injury and I can't get to class as quickly; I can't drive to classes because there are no nearby parking spots

There are more scripts in other sections of the book if you want to tap further on these issues. Check the Table of Contents for the corresponding page numbers.

Optional Emotions: Irritation; Overwhelmed; Rushed; Late/ never on time; Pushed

Section Four
Relationships

Navigating relationships is part of college. Meeting new people and making new friends can be as stressful as it can be fun. It can be hard to find people who understand you, and a group to belong to where you feel safe. If friendships fall apart, you experience the loss of someone important to you. The pain of loss results in stress. All of this applies equally to friendships as well as romantic relationships. Try the following scripts to help you through the various relationship issues you could face at college.

Connecting and Making Friends

Meeting and making friends can be a tough process. Maybe you want to be social but you haven't had much of an opportunity because you haven't connected with anyone on campus. Opening up to new people can make you feel vulnerable. Sometimes it may seem as if no one on campus fits with you and vice versa. It is a good idea to tap on all the emotions you are feeling so you can open up and meet those new friends, the ones everyone who's been to college says will be your buddies for life.

This script uses the Basic Recipe, but remember that you can use hand tapping and the gamut point when you are actually in the stressful social situation to help calm your nerves

1. **Because:** I haven't made any friends, connected with anyone to hang out with
2. **Emotion:** Insecure and shy, afraid to put myself out, what's wrong with me
3. **Sensation:** Tongue-tied
4. **Distress:** 0-10 ______

KC: Even though I am feeling insecure because I haven't made any friends since I got to college…everyone else has friends but me…I get all tongue-tied when I try to talk to anyone, **I accept myself and my feelings**.

KC: Even though I am feeling shy because I don't have anyone to hang out with, and I get tongue-tied when I do try to meet people, **I accept myself and how I feel.**

KC: Even though I feel insecure, afraid to put myself out, because I haven't met anyone I connect with yet, **I accept myself and my feelings**.

EB: I am feeling insecure
SE: I haven't made any friends at college
UE: I've tried but I haven't connected with anyone
UN: I'm feeling shy…afraid to put myself out again
CP: What's wrong with me anyway?
CB: Everyone else has made friends. Why can't I?
UA: I get so tongue-tied when I try to talk to new people
TH: Now I don't want to put myself out there again
EB: What if I am rejected?
SE: What if there isn't anyone there who will be my friend?
UE: No one for me to hang out with
UN: I get so tongue-tied when I try to talk to anyone new
CP: What is wrong with me?
CB: I feel so alone and insecure

UA: Feeling so insecure
TH: I haven't made any good friends, connected with anyone on campus

Keep tapping until the emotions settle down to a 2 or below. Now try a round or two of positive tapping. Sometimes, moving the energy in our systems, as EFT does, allows us to open up a space where we feel better and we send out more positive energy to others. By doing the positive tapping after releasing the distress, you might find that it is easier to meet people and make new connections.

EB: I feel pretty insecure right now
SE: Like I can't meet new people
UE: I get tongue-tied when I try to talk to someone new
UN: I feel alone and don't know anyone
CP: But I can make friends, I know that. After all, I had friends before coming here
CB: I know that I can make friends…other people do like me and are my friends
UA: Maybe it's just new here
TH: And maybe there are other people who are struggling too
EB: Maybe other people are having a tough time making friends like I am
SE: I'm open to letting my feelings of insecurity go
UE: Instead I will focus on remembering that I can be a good friend
UN: I have lots of good friends from before
CP: I choose to believe that I will make good friends here
CB: Even if it is hard to walk into a room alone
UA: I believe that I can meet people, that there is nothing wrong with me
TH: I choose to be confident
EB: I choose to be comfortable
SE: I choose to meet new people with ease

UE: Even if not everyone is my friend
UN: I choose to be friendly and open
CP: Maybe I will make a new friend today
CB: Maybe I won't
UA: But I choose to be friendly and open to the possibility
TH: That I can easily make new connections with quality people
EB: That I can feel secure about myself
SE: That there are people out there who want to be my friends
UE: People who are just waiting to meet me
UN: I choose to talk to a new person and not feel tongue-tied
CP: I choose to make it easy
CB: To enjoy the process
UA: To be confident that I will make new friends with ease
TH: I choose to feel the confidence inside of me

Tap on this script before you go into a social situation. It will open you up to the possibility of meeting new people.

Optional Because: Everyone I meet has other friends; I don't feel comfortable joining new groups; No one wants to be with me; No one ever asks me to join in; People here are unfriendly; I am always alone; No one likes me; I am too shy to meet anyone; I am a loner; I don't like anyone I have met since I arrived here; I haven't found anyone who likes the same things I do

There are more scripts in other sections of the book if you want to tap further on these issues. Check the Table of Contents for the corresponding page numbers.

Optional Emotions: Sad; Lonely; Fearful; Nervous; Apprehensive; Uptight; Not good enough; Alienated; Boring; Uncomfortable

Connecting and Trust

Meeting people at college is easy. Everyone is looking for friends. Making true friendships with people you trust is another matter. If you find you have not met anyone you can trust to be a true friend, try the next script. Take a deep breath and think about the emotions and physical sensations that come up for you around the ideas of connecting to and placing your trust in another person. Take some time to jot down what you are feeling and determine your level of distress. Add wording that will make the script specific to your thoughts, emotions and needs.

1. **Because:** I haven't found anyone on campus I can trust
2. **Emotions:** Sad and lonely
3. **Sensations:** Heartache
4. **Distress:** 0-10 _______

KC: Even though I am so sad and lonely because I am having such a hard time connecting with anyone on campus I can trust, **I accept myself.**

KC: Even though I can't find anyone I can truly trust and confide in and that makes me feel sad and lonely, I **accept myself.**

KC: Even though this is bringing up so many emotions and sensations in my body, **I accept myself and all I am feeling.**

EB: I can't connect with anyone on campus
SE: I can't find anyone I can truly trust and confide in
UE: I'm lonely and want that connection with someone here
UN: I don't know what to do
CP: I want to connect with someone, confide in someone, trust someone
CB: I feel it in my body…I feel it in my heart

UA: All these emotions I feel because I haven't connected with anyone
TH: I want to be able to trust someone who can be a true friend
EB: I'm open to finding that connection, I just don't know how to find it
SE: I just can't find anyone on campus to that I can trust to be a true friend and I feel sad
UE: I feel it in my heart…it aches
UN: I can't find someone I can trust and confide in
CP: I'm so lonely and I need that connection with someone
CB: I'm open to finding that connection, that trust
UA: I'm open to finding friends I can trust and confide in
TH: I'm open and ready to connect with people on campus

Take a deep breath. These are difficult emotions to feel, but tapping can help you acknowledge and accept the emotions you are feeling so that you will find it easier to open yourself to accepting friendship and trust. Keep tapping through this script, using it as a guide until you work through all your emotions and physical sensation surrounding connecting and trusting others.

Optional Because: It is hard for me to make new friends; It is hard for me to trust another person; Other people have hurt me before; Other people have broken trust with me in the past; I am shy and have a hard time connecting to other people

There are more scripts in other sections of the book if you want to tap further on these issues. Check the Table of Contents for the corresponding page numbers.

Optional Emotions: Hurt; Abandoned; Grief; Insecurity; Distrustful; Doubtful; Disillusioned; Shy; Alienated; Discouraged; Miserable

Not Sure How to Be More Social

Meeting people for the first time is nerve-wracking. Small talk can be difficult. Knowing what to say in order to make a good impression can feel impossible. There is always the niggling worry that you might say or do something that someone else won't like. If making new friends is difficult, for whatever reason, any worry you feel feeds on itself and hinders your ability to open up and make the friends you desire. Use this tapping script to help you relax. Change the wording to better reflect your personal situation. You may tap down one worry and find another one was hiding. Simply tap that one away as well. You can do this, whenever, wherever you need to. Don't forget that Hand Tapping is handy for those social situations when worries and doubts pop up and you don't want to look ridiculous tapping on your head.

Begin by taking a deep breath and assessing what emotions, body sensations and doubts come to you when thinking about a particular situation or just generally making friends. Jot them down and give them each a distress rating.

1. **Because:** I want to be more social but I don't know how...I might regret something I do or say
2. **Emotions:** Nervous, doubtful, worried
3. **Sensations:** Tired
4. **Distress:** 0-10 _______

KC: Even though I want to be more social, but I don't know how, **I accept myself**.

KC: Even though I'm afraid I'll say or do something I'll regret because I'm nervous around these new people, **I accept myself**.

KC: Even though I have all these doubts about making new friends, **I accept myself**.

EB: I want to be more social but I just don't know how
SE: I get so nervous around new people. What if I say or do something I'll regret?
UE: What if they make fun of me?
UN: I feel so left out...no one ever asks me to hang out
CP: I don't know how to find new friends
CB: I get so nervous around new people
UA: Sometimes, I'm just too tired to even try
TH: I'm afraid I'll do or say something I'll regret
EB: What if I try to make new friends and they don't want me?
SE: What if I'm just not good enough to be friends with them?
UE: What if I AM good enough to be friends with them?
UN: I just get so nervous
CP: I don't want to be pressured to change in order to fit in
CB: I want to be more social but I don't know how and no one asks me to hang out
UA: I have so many doubts about myself and being left out just makes them worse
TH: I'm open to being more social and making new friends
EB: I'm open to releasing my nerves and doubts
SE: I'm open to having fun and meeting new people
UE: But those doubts just creep back in when I meet new people
UN: Other people make new friends, no problem
CP: Why can't I?
CB: I'm open to making new friends
UA: I'm open to releasing the nerves and doubts, they don't help me in any way
TH: I'm open and ready to make new friends

Take a deep breath and notice how you are feeling. Has your distress level changed at all? Keep tapping through the script substituting the wording as needed. You will find this will help you relax and enjoy many new social, and even professional, relationships.

Optional Because: I'm nervous about needing people; I'm too shy and quiet; I'm not up on the latest fads

There are more scripts in other sections of the book if you want to tap further on these issues. Check the Table of Contents for the corresponding page numbers.

Optional Emotions: Pressured; Anxious; Lonely; Left out

I Don't Fit In

Everyone wants to find a place to belong. Even if you treasure how unique you are, it is always nice to have one or two other people who "get" you, understand the way you act, think and live your life. College is a great place to start over if you feel like you have been forced into a role in high school. But college can also be a daunting step when you are beginning anew without any support. It's a tricky balancing act, being true to you while finding your niche. As you journey into your true nature in college and find yourself floundering, take a moment to breathe in your truth, tap out the stress, and embrace the real you.

1. **Because:** No one gets me…I don't fit in
2. **Emotion:** Alone, isolated, hurt
3. **Sensation:** Awkward and clumsy
4. **Distress:** 0-10 ___________

KC: Even though I am alone and isolated on campus because no one here gets me and I don't fit in…I feel awkward around other people and so alone, **I am me and that's okay.** (repeat 3 times)

EB: I am alone
SE: Totally isolated on this campus
UE: Because no one gets me

UN: They call me weird…I don't fit in
CP: Even though I am just being me
CB: No one gets me
UA: No one accepts me for who I am
TH: Usually it doesn't bother me to be myself…to not fit in
EB: But I feel really alone here at college
SE: All on my own
UE: And isolated
UN: Because being me is different…I don't fit in
CP: But people say things like I am weird…and that hurts
CB: It is isolating, hurtful
UA: It hurts my feelings when they say that
TH: I feel clumsy and awkward around other people
EB: I feel so isolated and alone…I don't fit in
SE: Hurt by the comments, by what people say about me
UE: I want to be myself but it is hard to be alone
UN: I feel hurt and isolated…I don't fit in here
CP: I am just trying to be me, to find my niche
CB: But it feels like I will always be on my own
UA: And it hurts…I really don't fit in here
TH: Feeling so alone, so isolated…just for being me

Tap several rounds with this script. Pause and check in to see how you are feeling. Has anything changed? Do you feel less of the hurt or maybe do you feel it more? How about any new physical sensations? Jot down all that you feel and continue to tap, checking in every few rounds. Remember to check in after you think you are finished to ensure that you have released the emotions around your situation.

If you feel very isolated or have any other intense emotions, please be sure to visit your health services or counseling services for guidance as you sort out your emotions.

Optional Because: People make fun of me; People ignore me; No one wants to connect with me; I don't feel like it's okay to be me; What's wrong with me; I am an exchange student and no one else on campus is from my country; I am an exchange student, here for a semester, and I don't know if it is worth making friends for such a short time; I don't speak the language; I am a minority student and I feel very out of place on campus

There are more scripts in other sections of the book if you want to tap further on these issues. Check the Table of Contents for the corresponding page numbers.

Optional Emotions: Angry; Rejected; Judged; Sad; Frustrated; Insecure; Out of place; overwhelmed

Living Arrangements

Roommates can become great friends or they can make your life miserable. Hopefully, you have a wonderful relationship with your roommate, but, if not, here is a script to help you overcome the stress that may arise. Change the wording to fit your needs and use the name of your roommate to make the script more specific.

Take a deep breath and rate the intensity you feel when thinking about your relationship with your roommate. Think about where you feel physical sensations in your body as well as the emotions coming up like anger, frustration or upset.

1. **Because:** My living arrangement isn't working for me… my roommate is so annoying and doesn't respect my space…I hate going back to my room
2. **Emotions:** Anger, annoyance, stress
3. **Sensations:** Tightness in shoulders
4. **Distress:** 0-10 ________

KC: Even though I am angry because my living arrangement is causing me problems…my roommate, (name), is so annoying and doesn't respect my space, **I accept myself**.

KC: Even though this living arrangement isn't working for me, because (name) makes me so angry and does not respect my space, **I accept myself**.

KC: Even though there isn't anything I can do to change my roommate's behavior, I can only change my reaction, **I accept that and all my feelings.**

EB: I don't like my living arrangement
SE: I really wanted to like it but it just isn't working out
UE: My roommate annoys me so much…I hate going back to my room
UN: He/She is so disrespectful to me
CP: I don't understand why
CB: Why does he/she have to be such a jerk?
UA: *(Name of roommate)* is so disrespectful. This isn't working for me!
TH: My roommate doesn't respect my space
EB: It is so annoying…my shoulders tighten up as soon as I head back to my room
SE: *(Roommate name)* is so annoying because he/she doesn't respect my space
UE: This is not working for me! I don't need this stress
UN: I don't know what to do and I'm so annoyed
CP: All these issues with my roommate
CB: I just can't take it
UA: This living arrangement sucks
TH: This living arrangement is causing me problems

Take a deep breath and slowly release it. Was there anything specific that came up for you? Add in your specifics and tap another round of the script. Once your level of distress is at a 2 or lower, you may move to the next part.

EB: I want to get along with my roommate…I don't want there to be a problem
SE: I just don't know how to do that…(*Roommate name*) frustrates me so much!
UE: This isn't working out for me
UN: How can I make this work? Is there a way?
CP: I just don't know
CB: I'm open to finding a way to make my living arrangement work for me
UA: I'm putting too much time, money and effort into college to have a roommate issue ruin it
TH: How can I make this work for me?
EB: There must be a way
SE: What is the solution?
UE: I'm open to finding a solution to making this work for me
UN: How might I do that?
CP: What would I have to do?
CB: I'm open and ready to find a way to release this anger and annoyance with *(insert name)*
UA: I'm open to finding a way to make this living arrangement work
TH: I'm open to finding a solution that will work for both of us

Take a deep breath in and exhale. How are you feeling now? Perhaps some ideas came to you while you were tapping. Keep tapping and remain open. Sometimes changing your reaction will cause your roommate to change as well. Be open to communication.

Optional Because: My roommate doesn't respect my time: My roommate doesn't respect my privacy; My roommate is a slob; My roommate likes to party in the room even when I am asleep; My roommate goes to bed too early; My roommate stays up too late; My roommate is too loud; My roommate is always in the room and I never have any privacy; My roommate snores; My roommate always entertains overnight guests

Optional Emotions: Upset; Frustrated; Exhausted; Tense; Bitter; Hatred; Grouchy; Mad; Unhappy; Stuck

Pressure to Go out with Friends

Friendships change over time, growing, evolving and even dissolving. Friends may, intentionally or not, pressure you to do things you might not have done, for the better or for the worse. Use this script if you are having issues with your friends

We've offered a few tapping possibilities in the following script, but using your own wording is best. Tap into the emotions that are surrounding the issue and any physical sensations or places you hold that emotion in your body. Begin with a deep breath and assess your level of distress.

1. **Because:** My friend is pressuring me to go out all the time…I don't want to…I'm tired and I have work to do
2. **Emotions:** Stressed and frustrated
3. **Sensations:** Tired just thinking about it
4. **Distress:** 0-10 ________

KC: Even though I am stressed and frustrated because my friend is pressuring me to go out all the time, **I accept myself**.

KC: Even though my friend is pressuring me to go out every night and that makes me very stressed and frustrated because I am tired and I have work to do, **I accept myself and how I feel.**

KC: Even though I am stressed and frustrated because my friend keeps pressuring me to go out and party, but I don't want to, I **accept myself and my feelings**.

EB: My friend keeps pressuring me to go out every night
SE: I feel so stressed and frustrated
UE: I don't know what to do about it…what to tell him
UN: He keeps pressuring me to party every night
CP: But I don't want to because I have work to do and I am tired
CB: My friend just won't leave it alone…he keeps pressuring me to go out
UA: I feel so stressed and frustrated
TH: This issue with *(insert friend's name)*
EB: He keeps pressuring me to go out all the time
SE: I don't know what to do. I feel so stressed
UE: What should I do? How do I make him understand?
UN: I don't want to go out every night
CP: I have so much work to do and I am really tired
CB: But *(insert name)* keeps pressuring me to go out, to party, all the time
UA: I'm so stressed
TH: I feel so frustrated because of this issue with *(insert name)*

Take a deep breath and think about the situation. What is your distress rating now? If your level is still above a 2, try getting more specific about the situation, including any emotions or physical sensations that came up as you tapped. Have you encountered a similar situation in the past? If so, try tapping about that situation and see what happens. Sometimes your current emotions are triggered by past events. Tap away the old emotions and your reaction to your current issue may change for the better.

Optional Because: My friends are pressuring me to party; My friends are pressuring me to drink; My friends are pressuring me to do drugs; I caused drama with a friend and now I feel guilty; My old friendships at home aren't the same anymore; My friends aren't getting along and I feel stuck in the middle; Sometimes I do stupid things to impress my friends; I just don't want to be friends with *(insert name)*

There are more scripts in other sections of the book if you want to tap further on these issues. Check the Table of Contents for the corresponding page numbers.

Optional Emotions: Tension; Distress; Overwhelm; Turmoil; Pressured; Angry; Irritated; Powerless; Embarrassed; Ashamed; Dislike; Hatred

Significant Others

Being involved in a romantic relationship adds a new dimension to your life. A significant other or partner requires vulnerability, trust and openness. When you allow someone in, however, you also invite the possibility of betrayal and heartbreak. Even summoning the courage to approach someone you would like to ask out brings the possibility of rejection. On the other hand, perhaps you simply want to be in college, have friends, but not have to mess with the whole relationship thing. If all of your friends have a significant other, you might feel awkward or left out in social situations. Use this script to release the emotions you are having around this area of the relationship spectrum.

Being Rejected

1. **Because:** I asked someone out and she rejected me (we are using she here but substitute for your specific situation)
2. **Emotions:** Humiliation and Embarrassment
3. **Sensation:** Crawling skin...everyone's watching
4. **Distress:** 0-10 ________

KC: Even though I am humiliated and embarrassed because I asked (name of person) and she rejected me...I feel like everyone knows and I want to hide, **I accept myself and my feelings**. (repeat 3 times)

EB: I am so humiliated
SE: And embarrassed
UE: I asked *(name of person)* out and she said no
UN: She rejected me and I am so humiliated and embarrassed
CP: I wish I had never asked her out
CB: I just want to hide. I feel like everyone's watching...my skin is crawling
UA: I am so embarrassed, so humiliated
TH: She rejected me and I just want to hide

Repeat this script until you feel less distress. Add in details to help make it specific to you and your situation.

Optional Because: I don't want a boyfriend/girlfriend; I feel pressured to be in a relationship; Someone keeps asking me out but I don't want to go; I don't have time for a relationship; I am so lonely and I want to be in a relationship; I am in a relationship but I am not sure if he/she is the one; I want to tell someone that I care for them; I really like someone but he/she doesn't know that I exist; I don't want to hurt someone's feelings when I say no to going out with them

There are more scripts in other sections of the book if you want to tap further on these issues. Check the Table of Contents for the corresponding page numbers.

Optional Emotions: Pressured; Overwhelmed; Annoyed; Irritated; Alone; Lonely; Unhappy; Sad; Scared; Insecure

Ending a Relationship

This script covers some of the feelings you might have if you want to break up with your significant other. We are using "boyfriend" in this script but change the wording to meet your needs. We've added in a few things here that might be bothering you around this subject as well as listed a few more following the script. Add, subtract, make it your own.

1. **Because:** I don't want to be in this relationship anymore but I don't know how to break it off
2. **Emotions:** Frustrated, guilty
3. **Sensation:** (Include if you feel any physical sensations related to your emotions)
4. **Distress:** 0-10 ______

KC: Even though I am frustrated because I don't want to be in this relationship anymore but I don't know how to break it off, **I accept myself and how I feel.**

KC: Even though I feel guilty because I want to break up and I know I will hurt him if I do, **I accept myself and how I feel.**

KC: Even though I feel frustrated and guilty because I want to break up with my boyfriend and I don't know how to do it without hurting him, **I accept myself and how I feel.**

EB: I am frustrated
SE: I want to break up with my boyfriend but I don't know how to
UE: I feel guilty because I will hurt him
UN: I wish I could break up without hurting him
CP: But I know that breaking up with him is the right thing for me
CB: I don't know what to do
UA: I feel so frustrated and so guilty
TH: I know this relationship isn't working for me anymore
EB: I want out
SE: But I don't know how to tell him that I want to break up
UE: I don't know how to do it without hurting him
UN: I hate the idea of hurting him
CP: But I really do not want to stay in this relationship any longer
CB: I am so ready to get this over with
UA: Maybe I just have to do it
TH: Maybe it won't be as bad as I think
EB: What if he feels the same way?
SE: Whether he is hurt or not, I know that I have to end this
UE: I am open to letting this be easy
UN: Maybe it will be easier than I think
CP: I can do this even if it is hard
CB: I know it is for the best for me and for him
UA: I am not happy so I can't make him happy
TH: I am open to allowing this process to be easier than I think it will be…I know I can do this and that it is for the best

Take a deep breath and notice how you are feeling. Continue tapping through the script until your distress level has dropped to a 2 or below. You may choose to tap one final round saying the last line on each tapping point. This is a positive way to end your tapping session.

Optional Because: If I break up it will affect our mutual friends and relationships; Everyone expects us to stay together; He/she still loves me and I don't want to hurt them; I like someone else but don't know how to tell my current boyfriend/girlfriend; All my friends love this person, so why can't I; My parents love my boyfriend/girlfriend; I really do not have that much in common with this person; I am about to graduate and I want to be free to move on and pursue my dreams; This was fun for college but I don't want it to be permanent; My boyfriend/girlfriend frightens me**

Optional Emotions: Confused; Heartbroken; Stuck; Distressed; Remorseful; Resentful; Annoyed; Hopeless; Nervous; Scared

**If you are in an abusive relationship, please seek help. See Appendix C where you will find resources to guide you to get the help you need.

I Am Heartbroken

Recovering from a broken heart is not easy. Everyone says it just takes time, and, believe it or not, that is true. But when it happens to you, the "time" thing seems like a big lie. How can time heal such a massive wound, the breaking open of your heart, your very soul? Take some time for yourself to be alone and with other friends. Allow other people to support you as you heal. And use the following EFT script to help ease the pain. In this script, we are using "girlfriend" but change it to fit your situation.

1. **Because:** My girlfriend ended our relationship…I don't know how I will get over it
2. **Emotion:** Heartbroken, sad

3. **Sensation:** A hole in my heart, can't catch my breath when I think about it
4. **Distress:** 0-10 _________

KC: Even though I am heartbroken because my girlfriend broke up with me and I can't breathe when I think about her, **I accept myself and how I feel.**

KC: Even though there is a hole in my heart and I can't catch my breath because my girlfriend broke up with me…I thought were meant to be together, **I accept myself and how I feel.**

KC: Even though I am heartbroken and I don't know if I will ever get over this pain, because my girlfriend broke up with me…I can't breathe when I think about the breakup and being alone, **I accept myself and how I feel.**

EB: I am heartbroken
SE: My girlfriend broke up with me
UE: I love her
UN: I thought it was all okay
CP: And she broke it off
CB: She ended our relationship
UA: I have never felt this much pain before
TH: My heart feels like it is breaking. I can't catch my breath when I think about her
EB: I am heartbroken
SE: I thought we were doing fine, more than fine
UE: I love her so much
UN: How could she have broken up with me, left me?
CP: I can't believe this happened
CB: She hurt me so much…broke my heart
UA: It's so hard to breathe when I think about her
TH: Remembering all we had together

EB: And now it's gone and I'm heartbroken
SE: She ended it, our relationship
UE: She broke my heart, left me in so much pain
UN: I don't know if I will ever get over this
CP: My heart is broken…I can't breathe
CB: All this pain
UA: She ended it, broke up with me
TH: I am heartbroken, in so much pain…how do I get over this pain?

Take a deep breath and tune in to how you feel. If you are still feeling like the distress level is above a 2, tap a few more rounds on this script, adding in any additional insights, emotions, or physical sensations. Be sure to keep tapping until the distress has dropped. When you are ready, try the following short script to help you move on. Allow EFT and time to help you heal.

EB: I still feel a bit sad when I think of the break-up
SE: But I am open to moving on with my life
UE: I feel like it is time to go forward
UN: I have had time to grieve and I feel better
CP: I am feeling more like myself
CB: And I know that it is all going to be okay
UA: I am open to moving on with my life without my old girlfriend
TH: I am open to moving on with my life

Repeat as necessary. Take a deep breath and let it all sink in.

Optional Because: I don't know if my boyfriend/girlfriend is "the one"; I really like someone but they don't know that I exist; I asked someone out and he/she said "no"; I don't want to be in this relationship anymore; My other friendships will be affected if we break up; I feel pressured to have sex; He/she is so controlling; I don't like who I become when I am with my boyfriend/girlfriend; My issues from the last relationship are hurting my new relationship; He/she used me and hurt me; I am worried that my boyfriend/girlfriend is cheating on me

Optional Emotions: Confused; Rejected; Invisible or unseen; Alone; Pressured; In Turmoil; ; Stressed; Grief-stricken; Miserable; Angry; Betrayed

Section Five

Money

Money. Who doesn't feel a little stress when we think about the green stuff? It can feel like money is elusive, especially when you are in college and may be budgeting your own money for the first time. College forces you to make choices regarding money from the moment you decide to attend, including how to pay for school as well as how to budget once you're on campus. Below are several scripts to help you tap through the stress that accompanies money. Remember, money is a form of exchange which allows us to live life. Money can be fun and can pay for things we want and need. However, money can also be the source of a feeling of scarcity, of lack, and this can cause a great deal of distress. This is a good time to learn the important lessons around money. The first lesson is that we all must manage our money and this management is easier to do when stress levels are low. Releasing that stress allows us to be easier with our money, to spend it more mindfully, to use it for our best and highest good, and to find new ways to allow money to flow into our lives.

Use the following scripts to work through the emotions that might arise surrounding money. Use your own words or the suggestions following the scripts to make the tapping personal to your situation.

College Is So Expensive

College is expensive and that can cause stress as you prepare to head to school. Maybe you are still trying to figure out how to pay for your university years, waiting to hear from schools or outside agencies about scholarships or loans. Or maybe you know that, even with help, you'll still have to have a job in order to pay for your degree. Take a moment to sit quietly, eyes closed, and notice all the emotions you feel around money and paying for college. Also, notice if you feel or sense any of these emotions in any part of your physical body. Assess your distress level before you begin. Tap using the script below or substitute your own words. It is not the words you use as much as it is tapping and releasing the emotions that matter.

1. **Because:** Tuition is so expensive
2. **Emotions:** Worry
3. **Sensation:** Nauseous
4. **Distress:** 0-10 _______

KC: Even though I am worried because tuition is so expensive, and I feel nauseous when I think about paying for college, **I accept myself and how I feel**. (repeat 3 times)

EB: I'm worried about paying for college
SE: Tuition is so expensive
UE: I'm really worried and I feel nauseous when I think about it
UN: How am I going to pay for college with tuition as expensive as it is
CP: I am so worried...
CB: It's so much money...it makes me nauseous to think about it
UA: I'm worried and I feel it in my body, my stomach is nauseous
TH: I'm so worried, so nauseous, college is so expensive...

Keep tapping the points until your intensity drops to a 2 or below. Then check back in to make sure you have reduced your level of distress by taking a deep breath and thinking about paying for college. If any other emotions or sensations come up replace the words in the script and tap again. Come back here if you feel these emotions returning or other concerns around money surface.

Optional Because: I have to meet scholarship requirements; I have to meet financial aid requirements; I have to pay back loans after I graduate; I didn't get any scholarships or qualify for financial aid; Paying for college is hard for my parents; I have to pay for books; I have so many other expenses; Maybe I should get a job; I don't think I can handle a job and school; I need to learn to budget and I don't know how; I've never managed money before

There are more scripts in other sections of the book if you want to tap further on these issues. Check the Table of Contents for the corresponding page numbers.

Optional Emotions: Guilt; Fear; Anxiousness; Overwhelmed; Stressed; Confusion

I Have a Scholarship

If you have a scholarship for college, you may be concerned about meeting requirements so you do not lose your financial support. Knowing that you have to maintain a grade point average, be able to train and compete with a team, rehearse and perform in a choir or band, whatever those stipulations, they add more stress on top of an already stressful situation. Use the script below if you are feeling stressed about meeting scholarship requirements. Start with a deep breath and determine your level of distress.

1. **Because:** I have to meet scholarship requirements… maintain a particular grade point
2. **Emotions:** Scared…what if I can't do it

3. **Sensation:** Tightness in my chest
4. **Distress:** 0-10 ________

KC: Even though I am scared because I have to meet the scholarship requirements…I have to keep up my grades/train with the team/can't get injured/rehearse and perform…and I can't mess this up, all this makes my chest feel tight, **I accept myself and my feelings**. (repeat 3 times)

EB: I am so scared
SE: I have to keep my scholarship to afford school and there are so many requirements
UE: I have to maintain a *(fill in the %)* grade point average (or substitute the requirement for your scholarship)
UN: I'm so scared that I might mess up
CP: My chest gets tight thinking about all of this
CB: The requirements I have to meet to keep the scholarship
UA: I have to keep the scholarship to pay for school
TH: I am scared I might mess up, lose it

Take a deep breath and notice how you are feeling. Continue tapping through the script until your distress level has dropped to a 2 or below.

Optional Because: Just going to college is enough without all of these requirements; It's too much to handle it all; If I mess up I can't finish college; My parents would be so disappointed in me if I lost my scholarship; My parents can't afford to pay for college if I lose the scholarship; If I get injured I might lose my sports scholarship

There are more scripts in other sections of the book if you want to tap further on these issues. Check the Table of Contents for the corresponding page numbers.

Optional Emotions: Anxiousness; Stress; Overwhelm; Tension; Shame

I Feel Guilty Because my Parents Are Paying So Much

Many parents save for college for their kids. These funds are increasingly helpful as college costs skyrocket. Even with savings, paying for college can still be difficult. Many parents do not want to see their kids saddled with debt after graduation, even if it means they will sacrifice to make college payments. For you, the student, you may feel grateful to your parents but guilty accepting the money. Try the following script if you have any feelings of guilt centered around accepting money for college. Begin with a deep breath and assess your level of distress.

1. **Because:** My parents are paying for college; it's very expensive for them
2. **Emotion:** Guilty and stressed
3. **Sensation:** Headache
4. **Distress:** 0-10 ________

KC: Even though I feel guilty and stressed because my parents are paying for college and it is very expensive for them…it gives me a headache when I think about it, **I accept myself and my feelings.** (repeat 3 times)

EB: I feel guilty and stressed
SE: My parents are paying for college
UE: They are covering the costs my scholarships don't cover
UN: I know this is very expensive for them
CP: I am grateful but I also feel guilty
CB: I can't afford to let them down
UA: They are paying so much for me to be here
TH: I feel very guilty accepting their money

EB: Even though they tell me that they want to pay for college
SE: I still feel so guilty and so stressed taking their money
UE: I can't afford to let them down
UN: There is so much pressure on me to do well and it makes my head hurt
CP: I feel guilty and stressed
CB: Because my parents are covering my college costs
UA: My head hurts just thinking about the pressure I'm under
TH: I can't afford to let them down
EB: My parents believe in me and trust me to do well
SE: I appreciate their trust and I want to do well
UE: Maybe it is time to trust in myself
UN: To believe that I can do this
CP: I know that I will do my best
CB: I am very thankful to my parents for helping me out
UA: I am open to doing my best in college
TH: I am open to embracing this experience and being thankful for the opportunity…I know it will be okay

Take a deep breath and notice how you are feeling. Continue tapping through the script until your distress level has dropped to a 2 or below. You may choose to tap one final round saying the last line on each tapping point. This is a positive way to end your tapping session.

Optional Because: My parents have set strict guidelines that I have to meet; Money is tight at home; I know my parents cannot afford to pay for college; My parents tell me how hard this is for them; I know if finances change I won't be able to come back to college

Optional Emotions: Tense; Panicked; Terrified; Upset; Anxious

I Have to Work to Afford School

If you have to work in order to attend college, you have an added level of stress. Your friends might not understand how you feel if they are not in a similar situation. Take a deep breath and determine how your situation makes you feel. Note your emotions and the level of distress you are experiencing. Then use tapping to release your emotions so you can face your situation calmly from a centered place.

1. **Because:** I have to work so I can pay for school; my friends don't have to work
2. **Emotions:** Anger and frustration; it isn't fair
3. **Sensations:** Tension in shoulders and neck
4. **Distress:** 0-10 _______

KC: Even though I am angry because I have to work so that I can pay for school, and it isn't fair…I feel it in my neck and shoulders, **I accept myself and how I feel.**

KC: Even though I am angry and frustrated because I have to work so that I can pay for school and my friends don't have to work…this doesn't feel fair, **I accept myself and how I feel.**

KC: Even though I am angry and frustrated because I have to work to pay for school…I can't afford to go to school unless I hold down a job…and I feel this anger and frustration in my neck and shoulders, **I accept myself and how I feel.**

EB: I am so angry
SE: So damn angry and frustrated
UE: It isn't fair
UN: I want to have time for fun but I don't
CP: I have to work because I can't afford school unless I have a job

CB: It isn't fair
UA: None of my friends have to work
TH: Why do I have to work?
EB: All this anger and frustration is in my neck and shoulders
SE: I never have time for fun and it makes me so angry
UE: It isn't fair that I have to hold down a job while I go to college
UN: It is so stressful and it makes me angry, frustrated
CP: No one else has to do this much. They get to have fun
CB: All this stress, all this pressure makes me so angry, so frustrated
UA: It isn't fair that I have to work while I am going to school
TH: I never have time for fun…to relax…to be social
EB: But all of my friends do
SE: I don't want to do this anymore
UE: It is so stressful and it makes me so angry
UN: All this anger and frustration is in my neck and my shoulders
CP: So much pain in my neck and shoulders, so much anger and frustration
CB: It isn't fair, that I have to work, never get to have a social life
UA: No one else has all this stress, only me
TH: All this stress and frustration, all this pain in my neck and shoulders, it's not fair

Keep tapping until the intensity lowers. Change the wording to suit your situation and emotions.

Optional Because: I have to live at home to save money; My friends don't have to worry about money like I do; My friends can do what they want

Optional Emotions: Tension; Abandoned; Isolated; Alone; Lonely; Overwhelmed; Envious

Budgeting Money

Learning to budget money can be tricky. If the thought of budgeting your money sends you into a panic, try the script below. Start with a deep breath. Take a moment to identify the emotions you are feeling and then assess your level of distress. If you need to, change the words to fit your situation and give EFT a try.

1. **Because:** I have no idea how to budget my money, to pay for everything
2. **Emotion:** Scared and overwhelmed
3. **Sensation:** (Include if you feel any physical sensations related to your emotions)
4. **Distress:** 0-10________

KC: Even though I am feeling scared and overwhelmed because I have no idea how to budget my money, to pay for all the things I need at college, **I accept myself and how I feel.**

KC: Even though I am overwhelmed because I have to budget my money alone and it's scary…and I have so much to take care of, **I accept myself and how I feel.**

KC: Even though I am scared that I will screw it up because now I have to manage my money on my own, **I accept myself and how I feel**.

EB: I am so scared
SE: So overwhelmed
UE: I have to manage my money on my own
UN: I have to take care of books and eating out and social stuff with my money

CP: Have to budget it all
CB: And not run out
UA: But what if I screw it up?
TH: I am so scared I will screw it up
EB: What if I run out of money?
SE: Mess it all up and then run out of money
UE: I am so overwhelmed with money
UN: How do I budget
CP: Set my priorities
CB: I've never had to do this before
UA: And it is overwhelming
TH: I'm so overwhelmed, so scared, to take care of my money
EB: I have never had to do this before
SE: I have to set my money priorities
UE: To decide how to spend my money
UN: There is so much that I want to do and have to do with my money
CP: Books, clothes, social stuff, even eating out
CB: I don't know how to do this, to make the best choices
UA: And it is scary and overwhelming
TH: I feel scared about budgeting my money

Take a deep breath and assess your level of distress. Continue to tap, repeating this script, until your level of distress is a 2 or below.

Optional Because: My friends have more money than I do; I can't afford to do the things my friends can; I never have enough; Why can't my parents help me more; It is not fair that I have less; I am about to run out of money; I am out of money; My friends don't understand why I can't go out with them

Optional Emotions: Envious; Deprived; Embarrassed; Frustrated; Sad; Angry

Socializing, Money and Responsibility

Being social is an important and fun part of going to college. Until it becomes a burden because of money. It is easy to spend too much money on socializing in college. If you are having trouble managing your spending habits at school, try this script. Use your own words to personalize your tapping. Start with a deep breath, assess you level of distress, note any physical sensations, and tap it out.

1. **Because:** I am spending too much money being social…I need to be more responsible
2. **Emotions:** Out of control; upset
3. **Sensation:** (Include if you feel any physical sensations related to your emotions)
4. **Distress:** 0-10 ___________

KC: Even though I am upset and feeling out of control because I am spending too much money and I don't know how to stop…I need to be more responsible with my money, **I accept myself and my feelings**. (repeat 3 times)

EB: I am upset
SE: Out of control
UE: I am spending too much money being social
UN: And I don't know how to stop
CP: I need to be more responsible with my money
CB: But it is so hard and I can't control myself
UA: I am upset…out of control
TH: Spending way too much money going out with my friends
EB: Eating out, buying stuff
SE: I am out of control…I don't know how to stop
UE: I am so upset…I don't know what to do
UN: I can't stop this spending

CP: I am spending way too much going out with my friends
CB: It's got to stop and I don't know how
UA: I am out of control
TH: So upset, so out of control, spending way too much money

Tap until the intensity comes down. Releasing some of the stress will allow you to relax and make better decisions with your money.

Optional Because: I feel like I always get stuck with the paying for everything and it isn't fair; I wish I had money so I could socialize more; I feel left out because I can't afford things my friends can

Optional Emotions: Frightened; Angry; Irritated; Frustrated; Isolated; Abandoned: Sad; Panicked

Section Six

Physical and Emotional Health

College can take a toll on your mental, physical and emotional health, increasing the stress you experience. Studies indicate that up to ninety percent of doctor's visits are stress related.[16] Even weight gain can be related to stress. Even weight gain can be related to stress.

In this section, we have several scripts to help you cope with the stress of college. While the scripts are useful to release your emotions, and relax, they are not a substitute for your doctor's care. Contact the campus health and wellness services or your physician if you feel very ill. If you feel you are in an unstable emotional state or you are experiencing extreme stress, depression, intense anger, suicidal thoughts, or realize you cannot handle your emotions on your own, contact the college counseling services or a licensed mental health care professional immediately. Appendix C lists further resources you might find useful.

Taking Care of Myself

In college, you may be on your own for the first time. Take a moment to breathe deeply and tune into how you feel about this. What level of distress do you feel right now? Try tapping to relax and find your equilibrium. Use the script and add in or take out what isn't right for you.

1. **Because:** I have to take care of myself and I've never done it before
2. **Emotion:** Feeling overwhelmed
3. **Sensation:** Sick to my stomach
4. **Distress:** 0-10 __________

KC: Even though I am overwhelmed because I have to take care of myself, and I've never done that before…it feels like so much to do, **I accept myself and how I feel.**

KC: Even though I am overwhelmed because I have to do laundry and figure out food and I have never done that before, **I accept myself and how I feel.**

KC: Even though I am feeling totally overwhelmed because I have to take care of myself with no help…learn how to get around campus…to get up on time and get to classes, **I accept myself and how I feel.**

EB: I am overwhelmed
SE: I have to take care of myself on my own, all alone
UE: I've never had to do this alone before
UN: Mom and Dad aren't here to help me
CP: I feel totally overwhelmed
CB: I have to take care of myself…figure out my food and laundry…all of it alone
UA: I have to figure out how to get around and run errands
TH: I have to run all these errands, do all this stuff, and I don't have any time or support
EB: I'm so overwhelmed…I can't do it alone
SE: How do I get it all done?
UE: Get up on time and get to classes
UN: Do laundry
CP: Take care of me

CB: I am so overwhelmed and stressed
UA: I'm a lot to take care of and it's a lot to have to do
TH: I am feeling so overwhelmed…there is so much to do… taking care of me

Take a breath and reassess. Determine your level of distress and notice if you have any new emotions or sensations. If your distress level is still a 2 or higher, tap another round.

Optional Because: I can't budget my time; I have too much to do and no time to sleep; I have never done laundry before; I don't have a car and I'm trapped on campus; I'm running out of things I need; I don't have any clean underwear and no time to do laundry; I don't know how to do my banking and manage my money; I don't know how to cook (if living in an apartment)

There are more scripts in other sections of the book if you want to tap further on these issues. Check the Table of Contents for the corresponding page numbers.

Optional Emotions: Stuck; Trapped; Weak; Stressed; Distressed; Angry; Frustrated; Exhausted; Incompetent; Incapable

Sleep

You are tired. You have a big test tomorrow. You know you need to sleep but you can't stop thinking about the test. And you cannot fall asleep. Or maybe you did get to sleep initially but now you are awake, it is two in the morning, and you cannot fall back to sleep. It is frustrating when you are tossing and turning, especially when you know that you have an exam and need to be well -rested. Tapping can help whether you are having trouble getting to sleep or you are trying to get back to sleep.

This tapping method is a little different than the other scripts in this book. The act of tapping, while relaxing, can be stimulating, as well. When trying to sleep, we suggest simply pressing and holding gentle pressure at each point. Your movements should be slow and minimalistic. Whisper or think the wording in your head. The whole point is to relax your body and brain so you can get that sleep you so desperately need. As you get more comfortable with tapping, you can then simply imagine yourself pressure-pointing each spot to reduce movement even more when using EFT to help you sleep.

1. **Because:** I can't sleep
2. **Emotions:** Frustration, worry
3. **Sensations:** My mind is spinning
4. **Distress:** 1-10 ______

KC: Even though I can't sleep and I know I need to because I have a test tomorrow, **I accept myself.**

KC: Even though my mind is spinning and I can't sleep, **I accept myself.**

KC: Even though I'm getting really frustrated and worried because I can't sleep...I know I need to but I just can't, **I accept myself and all these feelings.**

EB: I can't sleep
SE: My mind is spinning
UE: I need to sleep because I have a test tomorrow
UN: I'm so frustrated
CP: I'm worried if I don't sleep, I'll fail my test
CB: I can't sleep. It's so frustrating
UA: My mind won't stop spinning

TH: I'm open to relaxing my mind and body so I can sleep
EB: I'm allowing my mind to relax and drift
SE: I'm drifting
UE: Relaxing and drifting
UN: Drifting
CP: Relaxing
CB: Drifting
UA: Drifting
TH: Drifting

Continue applying pressure slowly to each point as you repeat "Drifting" in your head. If you are still experiencing trouble sleeping, go back to the start of the script. Fill in with any wording that better suits your needs.

If you continue to have trouble sleeping, try tapping an hour before bedtime. Be specific, tapping on what has your mind racing. When you're ready for bed, use the script to relax and drift off.

Optional Because: I can't sleep because I'm so anxious; I can't sleep because I'm so nervous; I can't sleep because I'm so sad; I can't sleep because I don't feel well; I can't sleep because I'm so angry

Optional Emotions: Anxious; Nervous; Sad; Miserable; Angry

I Am So Sick

You're sick. Your nose is stuffed up, you have a hacking cough, and your throat hurts so badly that it's hard to swallow. Or maybe you've picked up that nasty twenty-four-hour stomach virus your roommate had a couple of days ago. You may be independent, away at college, grown up and on your own. But now, you want your mom.

Tapping might not be able to destroy the viruses that cause colds and stomach bugs, but it can help reduce the stress in your life and yes, stress can contribute to your illness. Because stress depresses your immune system, it inhibits your body's ability to fight invading viruses, leaving you more prone to illness.[17] Even if you are already sick, tap on how that makes you feel, along with any other stress you've been handling. You might be pleasantly surprised to discover that EFT helps you reduce not only your stress but the length of time that you are sick as well as the physical discomfort you experience. Start with a deep breath and take a moment to identify the emotion you are feeling and your distress level.

1. **Because:** I am sick and I want my mom
2. **Emotion:** I feel rotten…I want someone to take care of me
3. **Sensations:** Stuffy head, cough, sore throat, headache
4. **Distress:** 0-10 ________

KC: Even though feel rotten, like crap, because I am sick and I want my mom to take care of me, **I accept how I feel.**

KC: Even though I feel like crap because my head is stuffy, my throat hurts, I have a headache…I feel too bad to take care of myself, **I accept myself and how I feel.**

KC: Even though I feel absolutely rotten, because I have this awful cold, I want my mom, want someone to take care of me, **I accept myself and how I feel**.

EB: I feel like crap
SE: I have an awful cold and I feel rotten
UE: I feel so awful that I can't take care of myself
UN: I want my mom to take care of me
CP: I am so sick

CB: I feel awful, like crap
UA: My nose is stuffed up
TH: My throat hurts
EB: I am coughing and have a headache
SE: I feel rotten
UE: And I can't take care of myself…I'm too sick
UN: I want my mom…someone to take care of me
CP: Maybe I should go to health services but I don't feel like moving
CB: I have this rotten cold and I can't take care of myself
UA: My head hurts, my nose is stuffed up, I am coughing and have a sore throat
TH: I feel rotten and I want my mom

Once you've tapped on your physical symptoms and the emotions around them, you might recognize that some underlying stress has been depleting you, leaving you vulnerable to illness. Tap on any stressors that come up, whether the stress is from classes, a relationship, social obligations or work situations. Taking care of the underlying stress could give your body a boost to a speedier recovery.

EB: Wow, I just thought of that paper I had to write
SE: It was long, difficult, a real pain
UE: And worth a huge percentage of my grade
UN: I finally got it done, but I had to stay up all night to do it
CP: And I had a test the next day
CB: It was a really stressful time
UA: So much stress
TH: I've been under a lot of pressure lately
EB: So much pressure to get things done
SE: To do well in my classes
UE: My classes are really stressful

UN: These past few days were more stressful than usual
CP: My body is so tired
CB: Maybe that's partly why I got sick
UA: Because I've been so stressed, so tired
TH: All this stress, it has worn me out
EB: All this stress
SE: There is always so much to do
UE: The past few days have been even more stressful
UN: I've been under a lot of pressure lately
CP: My classes are really stressful
CB: My body is so tired, so worn out
UA: Maybe that is partly why I got so sick, because my body is so worn out
TH: All this stress

Keep tapping, releasing the stress. And once you bring that stress level down, take a long nap and allow your body time to rest and repair. Hope you feel better soon.

Optional Because: I have the flu; I broke a bone; I have a stomach virus; I think I need to go to the hospital

Optional Emotions: Exhausted; In pain; Angry; Frustrated; Terrified; Panicked

I Have the Blues

We all feel down from time to time. If you are having a down day, then try this script. We have added in a few reasons why you might be feeling less than stellar and more options are listed after the script. If, however, you have been feeling down and sad for a long time, and the feeling is getting worse, then please contact your campus counseling services or a licensed mental health care provider for professional guidance. It is important that you take care of yourself. Go to Appendix C where you will find a further list of resources.

1. **Because:** I have the blues and am feeling down
2. **Emotions:** Sad and down
3. **Sensation:** Listless, tired
4. **Distress:** 0-10___________

KC: Even though I am feeling sad and down in the dumps because I have the blues and I can't get happy...nothing feels quite right and I don't know why, but I am really tired and listless...I don't want to do anything, **I accept myself and how I feel**. (repeat 3 times)

EB: I have the blues
SE: I feel sad, down in the dumps
UE: Nothing is right and I don't know why
UN: I feel sad...down...not like myself
CP: I'm so sad and tired and listless
CB: I don't want to do anything
UA: I am just so tired and sad
TH: Feeling down in the dumps
EB: I have the blues and I feel sad
SE: Nothing is right and I don't know why
UE: Feeling sad, down in the dumps
UN: Just so tired and sad
CP: And I don't really know why
CB: Feeling sad
UA: Because I am down in the dumps, nothing is quite right
TH: I don't know why exactly, but I feel tired and sad

Tap through until you feel a shift in your emotions, your physical sensations or both. Now it is a good idea to tap the next two rounds to see if you can understand why you've been feeling down. Sometimes events cause emotional reactions in our bodies but we don't see the correlation at first. Discovery tapping like this can help you pinpoint what is going on.

EB: I wonder why I am feeling so down
SE: Why am I tired and listless
UE: Why I don't want to do anything
UN: This really is not like me
CP: Usually I like to be involved
CB: I like to hang out with friends and have fun
UA: But I have felt so blue lately
TH: Why have I been feeling this way…
EB: I am open to understanding why I feel so down
SE: To knowing or realizing what has made me feel so blue
UE: So out of sorts
UN: Maybe it is stress
CP: Or maybe something happened that started this mood
CB: Maybe it is something more
UA: I am open to understanding why I feel so down
TH: To finding the best way to release this blue mood

If you do realize that a particular event triggered your feelings, tap about that event and the emotions you feel when you think about it. See if the tapping helps you feel better, more like yourself. If you cannot uncover any underlying cause for your sadness, or tapping on the underlying cause doesn't help, please seek the help of a licensed mental health care professional. You might start at your campus counseling center. You can also go to Appendix C for a list of resources. All of your moods are part of you and sometimes you might feel a bit blue. If this blue mood can't be resolved, know that seeking help is the best course of action for your highest good.

Optional Because: My friend betrayed me; My boyfriend/girlfriend broke up with me; I have no friends/have not connected with other people; I'm scared to put myself out there and meet people; I am alone; I am exhausted; No one understands what I am going through; I have no one to talk to; I feel homesick; I miss my parents/friends/pets/boyfriend or girlfriend; I am using (food, drugs, alcohol, sex or other) to avoid feeling (insert the emotions you are experiencing)

There are more scripts in other sections of the book if you want to tap further on these issues. Check the Table of Contents for the corresponding page numbers.

Optional Emotions: Anger; Rage; Loneliness; Isolation/Isolated; Despair; Envy or Jealousy; Shyness; Fear; Out of balance; Overwhelmed; Frightened; Frenzied; Out of control

The Food on Campus

Dining Hall food isn't always tasty or healthy. Many people have dietary restrictions which aren't always met at the campus eating establishments. This can be not only frustrating and discouraging, it can also make you sick. Use the following script to tap out your concerns about the food on campus.

Take a deep breath and slowly release it. Now assess whatever is bothering you around food. Remember to substitute wording to meet your needs.

1. **Because:** The campus food is terrible…there aren't many options for me.
2. **Emotions:** Frustration, anger
3. **Sensations:** Stomach upset
4. **Distress:** 0-10 _______

KC: Even though I am frustrated because the food on campus is terrible and I never know what to eat, **I accept myself**.

KC: Even though I am so angry because the food on campus is so bad for me…it tastes terrible and my stomach hurts just thinking about it, **I accept myself**.

KC: Even though I can't eat this and it is so frustrating because there are no options for me on campus, **I accept myself and the situation**.

EB: I hate the food here and there aren't other options
SE: It is so bad for me…my stomach hurts just thinking about it
UE: It's so frustrating that there aren't other options
UN: It's so gross
CP: I hate the food here…It makes my stomach hurt so much
CB: The food on campus is so bad and I never know what to eat
UA: This is beyond frustrating…I really have no options
TH: I hate the food here…it's so hard to find something to eat
EB: What am I supposed to do?
SE: I end up spending money going out or ordering food
UE: This is so frustrating
UN: I hate this
CP: What am I supposed to eat?
CB: I can't deal with this, I'm so angry!
UA: How do other people eat this crap?
TH: I hate the food here

Take a breath and check back in to assess your level of distress. Keep tapping until you feel a release of intensity. You may have other feelings pop up. Be sure to include those in your tapping.

Remember, your tapping sessions can basically be a venting session, just keep tapping through the points as you vent. You'll be amazed at your ability to come up with alternative, creative solutions when you aren't overcome with emotion.

Optional Because: I have dietary restrictions that the dining hall cannot or will not accommodate; The food on campus makes me sick; The decent food on campus always runs out too fast; Dining hall hours never work with my schedule; I am getting fat eating the food on campus; I am losing weight because I cannot eat the food on campus

There are more scripts in other sections of the book if you want to tap further on these issues. Check the Table of Contents for the corresponding page numbers.

Optional Emotions: Irritation; Unhealthy; Disappointed; Miserable; Hungry; Furious; Grouchy

Food Cravings and Binges

Most of us have experienced cravings for a particular food. Cravings can feel as if they control us. EFT can help to calm the urge to splurge on a particular trigger food. Try the script for chocolate and substitute whatever food it is that you crave. Be specific. In the script, chocolate is described as smooth and creamy. If you crave chocolate and these aren't your adjectives, then choose ones that work better for you. If you love salty foods or crunchy foods, substitute the food and the descriptive words that trigger your cravings. In addition, it often helps to have the food in question with you as you tap so you can smell it and see it. You may be surprised, at the end of tapping, to find you don't want the food any more even though it is sitting in front of you.

Start by taking a deep inhalation and a long, smooth exhalation. Think about the chocolate, or other food, you love the most. If you have it with you, pick it up and smell it. Imagine taking a bite and how it would feel in your mouth. Do any physical sensations arise as you imagine eating your favorite trigger food? Invoking all the senses can make tapping to reduce cravings more successful.

1. **Because:** Intense cravings; I can't control myself around chocolate; I eat it whether I am hungry or not
2. **Emotions:** Feeling frantic and out of control
3. **Sensation:** I'm not in my body. I can't even feel my body.
4. **Distress:** 0-10

KC: Even though I feel frantic, because I can't control myself around chocolate...I keep eating it even when I'm not hungry...I love chocolate, how it tastes, how it smells, how creamy it is, **I accept myself and how I feel**.

KC: Even though I am totally out of control because I have such intense cravings for chocolate...I can't control myself around chocolate...I can't even feel my body, just this out of control craving, **I accept myself and how I feel.**

KC: Even though I am totally out of control and feeling frantic, because I have such intense cravings for chocolate...I love how it tastes, how it smells, and I eat it whether I am hungry or not, **I accept myself and how I feel**.

EB: These intense cravings for chocolate
SE: I love chocolate, everything about it
UE: I love the taste, the smell, how creamy and smooth it is
UN: When chocolate's around, I am totally out of control
CP: I eat chocolate whether I am hungry or not
CB: In fact, I can't even feel my body to know if I am hungry

UA: I just eat, no control, no stopping me
TH: Am I hungry?
EB: I don't even know because I can't feel my body, can't access how it feels
SE: Don't even know what hunger really feels like when I'm faced with chocolate cravings
UE: I just have to eat the chocolate
UN: I crave it…I love it
CP: I love everything about this chocolate
CB: I love the flavor
UA: I love the smell
TH: I love the way it looks and how creamy it tastes
EB: I simply have to eat it whether I am hungry or not
SE: If I know it is around, I definitely will eat it
UE: I love it so much
UN: I am frantic around this chocolate. I have no control around it
CP: I love it and I am going to eat it no matter what
CB: Even if chocolate isn't around I still crave it
UA: These cravings are so intense
TH: These cravings for chocolate are out of control

Stop here and assess where you are. How is that craving now? Has it decreased? Or are you ready to rip into the chocolate and throw this book away? Keep tapping until the intensity of the craving has been reduced. Then proceed on to the following script to add in some positive statements about you and your power over food choices.

EB: I wonder if I have to let the chocolate control me
SE: It has felt as if it controlled my life
UE: But I feel better now, not so frantic
UN: I wonder if it is possible to release this chocolate craving?

CP: I wonder if it is possible that chocolate doesn't have to control me?
CB: Maybe I can be in control of the chocolate and how much chocolate I eat
UA: I wonder if I can choose to eat the chocolate
TH: Or to not eat the chocolate
EB: To be the one in control over the chocolate
SE: That feels good
UE: I can choose to eat the chocolate
UN: I can choose to Not eat the chocolate
CP: I believe that it's possible that the choice is mine
CB: I can choose to eat chocolate when it feels good to eat it
UA: I can choose to release the out of control feelings I have about chocolate
TH: I can choose to eat chocolate…I don't have to eat it all
EB: I can choose to not eat chocolate, and I'm okay with that
SE: I choose to release the cravings
UE: And the frantic feelings around chocolate
UN: I choose to be calm and relaxed around chocolate
CP: To eat chocolate only when it feels right
CB: I choose to know I am in control of my eating…I don't have to eat it all and that's okay
UA: I now choose to eat for my highest and best good
TH: I now choose to eat food that is good for me, healthy for me, even chocolate, but only when I choose to eat it, for my highest good

Take a deep breath and slowly exhale. Tune into how you feel after tapping about your craving. Has the craving lessened or gone away? If not, keep tapping on the craving or any other emotion or physical sensation that came up for you. Once you have released the intensity of the craving to a 2 or below, you might try tapping through all the points repeating the last line in this script at each point. This is a positive way to end your tapping session.

Optional Because: Eating salty foods like chips or nuts; Eating fried foods; Eating all the time; Eating too much; Always hungry and always eating; Can't seem to eat enough; Drinking too much alcohol**

There are more scripts in other sections of the book if you want to tap further on these issues. Check the Table of Contents for the corresponding page numbers.

**Refer to Appendix C for additional resources if you think you have a drinking problem

Optional Emotions: Angry; Frustrated: Sad; Overwhelmed; Bored; Stressed; Helpless; Guilty; Ashamed; Lonely; Disconnected

Gaining Weight

Why is it that gaining weight in college seems to be as inevitable as papers and exams? There are many reasons for weight gain, but one factor contributing to those accumulating pounds is stress. Stress is an inescapable fact of life in college. Remember when we explained about the operation of the amygdala in your brain, the place where stress begins? The stress response causes the release of the hormone cortisol. Too much stress results in an overproduction of cortisol. Jessica Ortner, in her book The Tapping Solution for Weight Loss and Body Confidence, explains that weight gain has been attributed to this excess release of cortisol, with consequences ranging from increased appetite to sugar cravings, to additional belly fat.[18] One way to combat weight gain is to reduce stress, and what better, or easier way, to do this than with Tapping.

Of course, not only stress causes weight gain. Lack of exercise and poor food choices certainly don't help. The standard college diet, one which includes sodas and fries, chips and chocolate, with some real food sprinkled in, definitely contributes to those creeping pounds. Throw in socializing at parties or the local hang-out, where alcohol and fattening food abound, and it is no wonder college students gain weight. Added to it all, once you notice that your jeans feel a bit tighter, it is hard to feel comfortable, to relax in your body. With that discomfort comes that nasty imp, stress, back to wreak havoc with your amygdala.

Weight gain is not the only stress-related weight issue at college. As difficult as it is for people who are overweight to believe, there are other people with the opposite problem. Some people have a tough time because they lose weight easily and feel body-related judgment as a result. If your weight is weighing you down, try some tapping to release body-related stress. EFT helps to uncover what is at the root of those too many, or too few, pounds. Use the script below and adjust it for your personal situation. Be gentle and compassionate with yourself. If you find that your feelings are too much to handle alone, or if you think you may have an eating disorder, please seek support. You can start at your college's health and wellness office. Refer to Appendix C for additional resources regarding weight-related issues.

Script: Gaining weight

1. **Because:** I am gaining weight, feeling fat, and my clothes feel tight
2. **Emotion:** Shame, hate and disgust
3. **Sensation:** My skin feels tight and uncomfortable/I feel uncomfortable in my body
4. **Distress:** 0-10 __________

KC: Even though I am ashamed of my body and disgusted with myself because I am gaining weight…I feel uncomfortable in my body, **I accept myself and all of my feelings just as I am**.

KC: Even though I am gaining weight and my clothes feel tight, my skin feels tight and uncomfortable, and I am ashamed and disgusted with myself for gaining this weight, **I accept myself and all of my feelings just as I am.**

KC: Even though I am ashamed of my body and totally disgusted with myself, because I am gaining weight and my clothes feel so tight, **I accept myself just as I am.**

EB: I am gaining weight
SE: I feel so ashamed of my body
UE: I feel so fat and ashamed
UN: My skin feels tight and uncomfortable
CP: I am so ashamed of myself
CB: For gaining this weight
UA: I am totally disgusted with myself for allowing this to happen
TH: How has it happened anyway?
EB: How have I gained all this weight?
SE: I am ashamed of myself for the weight
UE: Ashamed of my body and how I look
UN: My clothes, my skin, feel tight
CP: I feel weird in my body, not like me
CB: I really hate how I look…I am so ashamed of myself
UA: I am so ashamed of this weight…of gaining all this weight
TH: I am ashamed and disgusted with myself and my body
EB: I am so ashamed of myself
SE: This body doesn't feel like mine
UE: It doesn't look like my body either
UN: I've gained weight and I am ashamed
CP: How could I have let this happened?
CB: I can't seem to stop eating
UA: I just eat and eat
TH: And I keep gaining weight

This can be a very emotional subject to address. Keep on tapping, adding in anything that comes up, like how stressed you are, how much you have to do, how you feel about the food that you overeat. Also, notice if you have any thoughts about what the food represents for you. Is the food comfort, a companion, a way to relieve stress, a way to avoid or resist something that you have to do? The following is a continuation of the script with a bit more added to it that might be helpful.

EB: I am so stressed out about this weight
SE: Why do I eat so much?
UE: What is the eating all about?
UN: I didn't eat this much at home
CP: But I wasn't as stressed at home
CB: I have so much to do here at school
UA: It's all so much more stressful
TH: I never get a break
EB: When I do get a break I eat whether I am alone, with friends or out for fun
SE: We eat...it's a social thing
UE: I eat when I need a break...I grab <u>(food of choice)</u>
UN: Food can be so comforting
CP: Sometimes I eat because I have too much to do and I need a break/I am avoiding my work
CB: Sometimes I feel lonely and I eat
UA: Food can be a friend, it's always there
TH: When did this get so complicated?
EB: I wish I could only eat when I am hungry
SE: I am sick of eating all this junk but I can't stop
UE: It's so easy to eat when I am stressed or even bored
UN: It's so easy to eat when I am lonely or sad
CP: I am so ashamed that I eat so much but it's hard to stop
CB: Ashamed and disgusted with myself

UA: All this shame and disgust because I have gained weight
TH: I am so ashamed, so disgusted

Once you have tapped on this script, adding whatever feels true for you, take a moment to assess your level of distress. Close your eyes and notice how you feel and if any new feelings have emerged. Once you have reduced the level of distress to a 2 or below, try tapping on the continuation of the script below to add in some positive statements.

EB: I am feeling a bit better now
SE: My stress level is down
UE: I'm open to finding ways to reduce stress and care for myself besides food
UN: I can continue to tap
CP: I can take a walk or call a friend
CB: I can take a few deep breaths to relax
UA: I can also choose to eat if I need to
TH: Because I have to have food to fuel my body
EB: But now I know that I can choose to eat healthy food
SE: I don't have to eat the foods that cause me to feel bad and gain weight
UE: I can choose to eat those foods
UN: But I can also choose to not eat those foods
CP: It is up to me. I am the one in control, not the food
CB: I choose to eat healthfully and to be calm as I decide how to feed my body
UA: I now choose to be okay and to select the food that nourishes me
TH: I now choose to release the stress, the shame and this extra weight. I now choose to calmly and easily eat for my health and wellbeing and to select food that nourishes me for my highest good.

Take a deep breath and notice how you are feeling. If you want to continue tapping, try tapping on all the points saying the last statement at every point. This is a very positive way to complete your tapping session.

Optional Because: I can't stop eating; I can't lose weight; What's wrong with me; My clothes don't fit; I don't look good; No one will like me; I will never get a date; Who would want to be seen with me; I don't want to be seen by anyone; I don't want to be in this body; My body is huge; I am fat and ugly; I don't care how I look anymore, I just want to eat what I want; I am avoiding people and situations because of my weight; I drink too much alcohol and it is causing me to gain weight; I can never find time to exercise; I am purging in order to stay thin; The food at school is disgusting; I am losing weight; I hate how skinny I am; I am not eating because the food is so nasty; I can't bring myself to eat here; I can't do *(what are you avoiding because of your weight)* until I lose weight/gain weight. **

There are more scripts in other sections of the book if you want to tap further on these issues. Check the Table of Contents for the corresponding page numbers.

**Refer to Appendix C for additional resources if you think you have a drinking problem or an eating disorder

Optional Emotions: Weak-willed; Frenzied; Frantic; Out-of-control; Angry; Judgmental-of-self; Stressed-out; Frustrated; Disgusted; Despairing; Embarrassed; Isolated; Alone; Panicked; Terrified

Excessive Drinking or Drug Use

If you think you may have a problem with excessive drinking or drug use, we strongly encourage you to seek medical treatment immediately as this book and tapping are not substitutes for the professional help you may need. You may want to start with a visit to your campus health and wellness center. Taking the first step in this situation is often the hardest. Use this tapping script to help you as you begin this journey. Start with a deep inhalation and exhalation. Write down all the emotions you are feeling, including the distress rating for each. Check in with your body and see where you are feeling these emotions. Describe and rate those sensations. Take time to really tune into yourself. It is vital that you take this time to make yourself the top priority.

1. **Because:** I might have a drinking problem…I don't know how to get help…I don't know if I want to get help
2. **Emotions:** Worried, distraught, confused and afraid
3. **Sensations:** (Include if you feel any physical sensations related to your emotions)
4. **Distress:** 0-10 _______

KC: Even though I am worried and afraid that I might have a drinking problem and I don't know what to do, **I accept myself**.

KC: Even though I am really scared that I have a problem and I don't know where to start to get help, **I accept myself**.

KC: Even though I worry that I have a drinking problem…I don't know if I'm ready to get help, or if I even want to, and that scares me, **I accept myself and all my feelings**.

EB: I'm worried I might have a drinking problem
SE: I don't know what to do about it
UE: I can't control myself and that scares me
UN: I'm worried I might have a drinking problem
CP: I don't know how to get help with this…I don't know that I want to get help

CB: I don't think I can stop drinking
UA: What would I say to my friends?
TH: Who would I be if I didn't drink?
EB: I think life is easier to deal with when I drink...I can't make it through the day if I don't
SE: That scares me...I think I have a problem but I don't know what to do or if I want to do anything
UE: I worry that drinking might be ruining my life
UN: I've tried not to drink...it's so hard. I can't do it...I need it
CP: Drinking is what I do to have fun...to chill out
CB: But I'm worried I have a problem because I just can't stop. What should I do?
UA: I'm scared I have a problem
TH: I'm worried I might have a drinking problem and that really scares me. I just don't know what to do

Take a deep breath in and let that out. This is a big deal! Check in with all the emotions and body sensations you are having. Continue tapping until your intensity level is lower than a 2. Once there, you can move onto the next script.

EB: I'm scared and worried I have a problem with drinking
SE: I don't know what to do
UE: But I am choosing to be open to getting the help that I may need
UN: I'm so scared and worried...what if I can't stop?
CP: I don't know where to get the help I may need
CB: But I'm choosing now to be open to receiving that help
UA: I'm so worried and so scared
TH: I don't know where to start to find the help I may need
EB: What if no one supports me?
SE: But, what if everyone supports me?
UE: I don't know if I can do this

UN: I'm choosing to be open to receiving help
CP: I just don't know who to turn to for support
CB: But I am open to finding a way
UA: I'm just so scared and worried that I have a drinking problem
TH: I am choosing now to be open to receiving the help I may need

Take a deep breath and let it out. It is difficult to ask for help but being open to finding support will make the healing process easier. We suggest you start with calling or visiting your campus' health services or look online for assistance. The professionals there will be able to get you the assistance you need. Refer to Appendix C for more resources.

Optional Because: I have a drug problem; I don't know where to turn; I am out of control; I can't believe I let this happen; My parents will be disappointed in me; I can't admit this problem; This is too big to handle; I don't want to stop; I don't think I can stop; I don't want to go to rehab; I don't want to be the only one of my friends who can't drink/do drugs; Maybe I am blowing this out of proportion; I am drinking/doing drugs and missing class; I am about to get thrown out of college because my grades have suffered

Optional Emotions: Shame; Guilt; Remorse; Embarrassment; Out-of-control; Desperate; Suffering; Withdrawn; Alone

I Am Worried About a Friend who is Drinking/ Taking Drugs

You may have a friend in college who is partying too much. This can be worrisome and heartbreaking to watch. You may try to help or offer advice, but your well-meaning suggestions often go unheard or are angrily rebuffed. Here is a script to help you cope should you find yourself in this situation.

Take a deep breath in and focus on the problem. Think of the emotions that come up for you when you think about your friend and their problem. Consider any incidents that have occurred because of their excessive drinking/drug use.

1. **Because:** My friend is taking drugs excessively…It is changing who they are…I don't know how to help them
2. **Emotions:** Worried, scared, helpless
3. **Sensations:** (Include if you feel any physical sensations related to your emotions)
4. **Distress:** 0-10 ________

KC: Even though I am so worried about (insert name) because they are using drugs too much and it is changing who they are…I miss my friend and I want to help them but I don't know how, **I accept myself**.

KC: Even though I am really scared that (insert name) is messing up his life and I don't know how to help him/her, **I accept myself and I accept (insert name)**.

KC: Even though I don't know how to help (insert name) without hurting their feelings or ruining our friendship, and I feel scared and helpless, **I accept myself and all these feelings**.

EB: I'm so worried about *(insert name)*
SE: I think he needs help but I don't know how to do that
UE: It makes me so mad to watch him mess up his life this way
UN: How can I help *(insert name)* without ruining our friendship?

CP: I can't say, "Hey, you have a drug problem, let's get you some help." Can I?
CB: What if he hates me forever?
UA: I don't know what to do and I'm so worried about him
TH: My friend has a problem and I don't know how to help or even if I should
EB: I am so worried for him and so scared…it makes me angry to watch him mess up his life
SE: What should I do?
UE: I wish I knew
UN: I get so mad when I watch what he does
CP: This has to stop, but how?
CB: Should I chance our friendship and try to help?
UA: I want to help…I just don't know how
TH: I am so worried about *(insert name)*…his drug use has gotten out of hand

Take a deep breath in and a long breath out. Check the intensity now. Have your emotions shifted to something different? Do you feel your emotions in your physical body? Try adding those sensations to the tapping script and change the wording to reflect how you feel. It is helpful to include some incidents that have occurred with this friend in your tapping. Tap about the emotions you felt during that incident. Do you think your friend might try to terminate your friendship if you step in to help? Why do you think that? Tap about that as well. There is no right or wrong answer when it comes to helping a friend with a substance abuse problem, but identifying and releasing your emotions is a healthy step in being able to offer them the support they need.

Optional Because: My friend is always drunk or high; My friend has a drinking problem; My friend is hanging out with a bad crowd; I don't want to be with my friend anymore; I don't want to live with this person anymore but I am stuck; My friend is abusive when he/she is drunk or high; My friend is sick from all the drinking/drugs; My friend could overdose **

There are more scripts in other sections of the book if you want to tap further on these issues. Check the Table of Contents for the corresponding page numbers.

**Refer to Appendix C for additional resources.

Optional Emotions: Frustrated; Angry; Afraid; Concerned; Terrified; Desperate

Section Seven
Transitions

Leaving home to go to college is a transition, whether you are beginning your university years, or well into college. It can feel like you get settled at home or on campus and then you have to leave. You may never want to leave home and family or you may never want to leave campus and your friends. We have several scripts in this section to assist you in releasing unsettling emotions.

Leaving Home for College

Begin with a deep inhale and long exhale. Sense how you feel. Notice your emotions around the transition you are experiencing. What are those emotions? You may want make a note of them. Now tune into your body. Do you have any physical sensations accompanying your emotions? Take time to assess your level of distress before you begin to tap it out.

1. **Because**: I'm leaving home for college…I might not like it
2. **Emotion:** Scared or fearful
3. **Sensation:** Tightness in chest
4. **Distress:** 0-10 _______

KC: Even though I'm scared because I am leaving home for college and it's all so new and I might not like it, **I accept myself and how I feel.**

KC: Even though I am scared and I have tightness in my chest, because I am leaving home for college...what if I don't like it, **I accept myself and how I feel.**

KC: Even though I am scared because I am leaving home for college...I feel the fear in my chest...it's so tight when I think about leaving home, **I accept myself and how I feel.**

EB: I'm scared about leaving for college
SE: Because it's all so new
UE: I'm really scared
UN: I might not like it at college
CP: This fear
CB: It's so strong
UA: I am so scared my chest feels tight
TH: All this fear in my chest because I am leaving for college, and I might not like it

Repeat the tapping until the emotions you are feeling lessen. Take a moment to breathe in as you contemplate leaving home. How are you feeling now? Have any new emotions or physical sensations surfaced? Continue to tap through the script, adding in anything new that you are feeling. See if you can bring down the emotion to a 2 or below.

Once you have reduced your distress level to a 2, it might be nice to add in some positive statements, as in the following script.

EB: I feel better now, less scared
SE: Now I can remember why I chose to go away to college
UE: All the excitement that I felt when I visited campus/chose this school
UN: I am open to remembering all these positive feelings
CP: I open to feeling that way again

CB: I know it is going to be a big change to go away to college
UA: But I choose to be positive, to remember all the good things about this choice I made
TH: And to know that I can come back here, tap again, if I feel the fear or any other emotion

Optional Because: I will miss my parents; I will miss my siblings; I will miss my friends; I will miss my boyfriend/girlfriend; I'm done with school and I don't want to start over again; I am going so far away; I won't know anyone there; What if I don't make friends; I will be stuck there

Optional Emotions: Worry; Anxiousness; Anticipation; Grief; Sadness; Overwhelm; Stress; Anger; Tension; Petrified; Alone; Stuck; Insecurity

Homesick

It is never easy to move. Moving for college, especially for the first time, can be especially unsettling. This may be your first step into the real world without parents or guardians to guide you. You may still feel homesick returning to college even if you not in your first year. There are many adjustments you will have to make as you settle into college life. Try the following tapping script if you are feeling homesick.

Start with a deep breath and notice what emotions are surfacing. Take time to assess your level of distress and to notice if you have any physical sensations accompanying the emotions. It is time to tap it out.

1. **Because**: I am homesick…I miss home and I miss my parents
2. **Emotion:** Sad and lonely

3. **Sensation:** My throat feels tight…I want to cry
4. **Distress:** 0-10 _______

KC: Even though I am sad and lonely because I am homesick… my throat feels tight, **I accept myself and how I feel.** (repeat 3 times)

EB: I am so sad
SE: Because I am homesick
UE: I really miss home
UN: I am so homesick
CP: My throat feels tight, like I want to cry
CB: I am so homesick
UA: My throat is tight, like I am going to cry…I am so very sad and homesick
TH: I miss home, feeling so sad, so homesick

Keep tapping and make it more specific and describe exactly what makes you feel homesick. Use the following script or add your own words as you continue to tap.

EB: I feel sad because I am homesick
SE: I miss my parents
UE: It's so hard to be away from home, from familiar people and places
UN: It's so hard to meet new people
CP: My throat is tight…I feel like I'm going to cry
CB: I miss home so much
UA: I am really homesick and sad
TH: Feeling so sad, and my throat is tight, I want to cry

Continue tapping until your level of distress falls to a 2 or below. Take a deep breath and check back in to see how you feel when you think about being away from home. Continue tapping, adding in any shifts in your emotions or sensations, until you have succeeded in lessening your level of distress.

Optional Because: I feel so far away from home; I am too far away from home; No one is here to help me; I have to do it all alone; I haven't connected with anyone; I miss my friends; I miss my pets; I miss my boyfriend or girlfriend; I miss my own space

Optional Emotions: Lonely; Afraid; Lost and alone; Unhappy; Stressed; Overwhelmed; Unwelcome; Distressed; Vulnerable

I Don't Want to Go Home

1. **Because:** I don't want to go home…I'll have to follow my parents' rules…they won't see that I've grown up
2. **Emotions:** Anger and irritation
3. **Sensations:** (Include if you feel any physical sensations related to your emotions)
4. **Distress:** 0-10 ______

KC: Even though I am angry because I have to go home and follow my parents' rules, and they won't see that I have grown up, **I accept myself and how I feel.**

KC: Even though I am angry and irritated because I've been on my own, independent at school, and now I have to go home and follow my parents' rules, **I accept myself and how I feel**.

KC: Even though I am very angry and irritated because I have to go home and I don't want to, don't want to follow my parents' rules, I've been independent all year and now I won't be, **I accept myself and how I feel**.

EB: I am so angry
SE: I have to go home

UE: And I know I will have to follow my parents' rules
UN: Even though I have been independent all year at school
CP: But they'll insist I follow their rules
CB: Won't recognize that I am grown, independent
UA: They'll probably treat me like the kid I was
TH: Not like the adult that I've become
EB: And that makes me angry, irritated
SE: It isn't fair
UE: Because I've grown up...grown out of their rules
UN: But I'll be forced to follow those rules no matter that I'm grown up
CP: They won't see that I am independent, capable, grown
CB: They'll see the kid and make stupid kid rules
UA: And that makes me angry, irritated
TH: I am angry because I don't want to go home and follow my parents' rules

Once you have tapped, check to see where you distress level is. Has it dropped? How are you feeling now about going home? Have any new emotions surfaced? Once you have identified and tapped out all that is troubling you about returning home, see if the next script, adding in some positive statements, is helpful. Perhaps, if you approach your parents with positive ideas for structuring your visit, things will be easier, calmer, and more pleasant, allowing you to enjoy the time with your family.

EB: I am still not sure about going home
SE: Not convinced that it will be okay
UE: But I am open to the idea that I can talk to my parents
UN: I am open to the possibility that we can discuss the rules for my visit home
CP: And that they may listen to what I have to say
CB: May allow me to help structure the visit so it works for all of us

UA: I am open to the possibility that things won't be as bad as I think they will
TH: Maybe my parents can be reasonable and listen to me
EB: I choose to be open to listening to my parents
SE: I choose to try and understand their point of view
UE: And to calmly explain my point of view and what I need during my visit
UN: I am open to being a part of my family while I'm home
CP: And to compromising with my parents, to sharing, listening, hearing
CB: I am open to the possibility that they will listen and hear me
UA: I choose to be optimistic about this visit home, that my parents and I can work together
TH: I am open to both sides being flexible and understanding so we can all enjoy the time together

Optional Because: My parents won't listen to me; My parents stifle me, shut down my voice; I never enjoy being at home, not even before; I can't do what I want at home; My parents treat me like a child; My parents control every part of my life when I am at home; My friendships/relationships at home have changed; None of my old friends are coming home for the summer; I will be all alone; I will miss my friends at college

Optional Emotions: Stifled; Pissed; Tense; Frustrated; Worried; Lonely; Bored; Sad

I Don't Want to Go Back to College

College is fun, wonderful, exciting, full of lots of great people…except when it's not. Maybe you are not happy at school. Perhaps you thought that, after a break at home, you would be fine to return.

Now you find that you want to stay home, close to your parents, your old friends, and all that is familiar.

If you are feeling stressed over the thought of returning to campus, it may be time to have a chat with your folks. Being away from home for college is not for everyone. If your present college situation is not working for you, it might be time to consider other options. Be honest with your parents. College is your experience to enjoy and often, just by talking, solutions come to what might seem to be the thorniest problems. If you are considering transferring to a new college, take a look in Section Nine for a useful script.

Begin with a deep breath. Determine how you are feeling and your level of distress. Notice if you feel any physical sensations associated with your problem. It's time to tap.

1. **Because:** I have to go back to college but I really don't want to
2. **Emotion:** Sadness
3. **Sensation:** Choking feeling in my throat, crying
4. **Distress:** 0-10

KC: Even though I feel sad because I have to go back to college soon and I don't want to...I feel a choking in my throat when I think about it, **I accept myself and all of my feelings.**

KC: Even though I feel so sad that it makes me cry because I don't want to go back to college but I have to go soon, **I accept myself and all of my feelings**.

KC: Even though I feel sad because I have to go back to college soon but I really don't want to...I wish I had said something sooner because this feels like the wrong thing to do, and it makes me sad, **I accept myself and all of my feelings.**

EB: I feel so sad and it makes me cry
SE: I don't want to go back to college
UE: But I have to go soon, sooner than I'd like
UN: I really don't want to go back at all
CP: I feel sad…choked in my throat…when I think about it
CB: I feel so sad
UA: I wish I had said something sooner
TH: Told them I was unhappy at college
EB: Because now it feels like it's too late to change
SE: But I really don't want to go back to college
UE: I feel so sad and I cry when I think about it
UN: Feeling so sad, so choked in my throat
CP: When I think about going all that way back to college
CB: I am not happy there…I wish I had made a change
UA: But it feels like it's too late…I have to go back
TH: And I am feeling so sad, so choked up…crying when I think about going back to college

Tap down your level of distress and check in to see what you feel. Do you feel more calm? Did you discover that you are simply sad to leave home but maybe, a part of you is excited to return? Or are you still very distressed? Is it time to talk to your parents or a trusted adult about this situation? Remember that, even though you are now an adult, sometimes even adults need guidance and support. Try the next script to find some calm before you talk to your parents if you are certain that going back to school is not the right answer for you. And don't forget to use the Hand Tapping points as you talk to your parents.

EB: I still don't want to go back to college
SE: But I am feeling better about it

UE: I think I need to talk to someone about how I feel
UN: I haven't wanted to upset anyone so I've kept it to myself
CP: But I can't finish the rest of college feeling like this
CB: It's too hard to feel this way
UA: And college is too much to handle if I am upset about being there
TH: I hope my parents aren't mad at me
EB: I am open to finding a solution with their help
SE: I am open to doing whatever I need to do to make it all work
UE: I am open to the possibility that my parents will understand how I am feeling
UN: I have kept this to myself for too long
CP: And I still don't really want to go back
CB: I choose to believe that there is a way to solve this even though I don't know how right now
UA: I choose to trust that my parents will listen to me and guide me
TH: I choose to be open to guidance from any source to work out this situation
EB: I choose to make this easy and calm
SE: I choose to trust that there is an answer to this problem
UE: I know it is time to talk to my parents about this
UN: And I choose to trust that we can discuss this
CP: That there is an answer even though it feels impossible
CB: I am open to finding that answer even though I don't know what it is right now
UA: I am open to any guidance I can get to work out this situation
TH: I choose to make this process easy, calm, and to allow it to work out for my best good

Optional Because: I am scared to go back to school; College frightens me; I don't have any friends to go back to; I'm conflicted because I want to stay home when I'm home but I also want to be back in college when I am there; I miss my parents/friends/boyfriend or girlfriend/pets/siblings when I am gone

There are more scripts in other sections of the book if you want to tap further on these issues. Check the Table of Contents for the corresponding page numbers.

Optional Emotions: Fear; Homesickness; Loneliness; Confused; Without options; Frustrated; Unhappy

I Don't Have a Job So I Have to Go Home

College is finished and it's time for a job or an internship. You've searched diligently, but you have not been able to find either. Your only option is to return home and look for a job...for something to tide you over until a better situation comes along. Moving back home to your parents' rules and your childhood room might be more than a little stressful. If you are in this situation, try the following script.

Start with a deep breath. What emotions are you feeling? Do you have any physical sensations accompanying your emotions? Determine your level of distress and begin tapping. Substitute your own words if the ones in the script are not quite right.

1. **Because:** College is over and I don't have a job...I have to return home to live
2. **Emotion:** Irritation and anger
3. **Sensation:** Tension in jaw and clenching
4. **Distress:** 0-10 ______

KC: Even though I am irritated because I have to go home to live...I don't have a job yet, so I can't afford my own place to live, **I accept myself and my feelings**.

KC: Even though I am feeling angry because I have to go home to live, back with my parents, to my old room, and I really want my own place, but I don't have a job or a way to pay rent, **I accept myself and my feelings.**

KC: Even though I am irritated and angry because I have to go home to live and I feel tension in my jaw...I keep clenching my teeth when I think about this, **I accept myself and how I feel**.

EB: I am irritated
SE: And angry
UE: Because I have to go home after graduation
UN: I have to live at home and that is so irritating
CP: I don't have a job so I can't afford rent
CB: But I really don't want to live with my family again
UA: All the rules
TH: The lack of privacy
EB: I am so angry that I have to go home
SE: Why couldn't I find a job?
UE: I want to be on my own
UN: But I have to live at home after all this time away
CP: I've outgrown home
CB: It's time to be on my own but I can't, not yet
UA: So irritated and angry that I have to move back home after graduation
TH: I'm irritated and angry that I have to move back home

Optional Because: My parents have so many rules and I'm an adult; I am the only person I know who has to move back home; I hate being at home; I am too old to be at home; I've outgrown my room and my parents' rules; I am the only person who doesn't have a job; I can't find an internship

There are more scripts in other sections of the book if you want to tap further on these issues. Check the Table of Contents for the corresponding page numbers.

Optional Emotions: Dread; Frustrated; Sad; Embarrassed; Ridiculous; Stupid; Unhappy; Ashamed; Inept; Uncomfortable; Resentful

Section Eight
Preparing for the Real World

Graduation is nearing. All your hard work will finally pay off. The future looms, bright, exciting, and scary as hell. Perhaps you are looking for a job or an internship. Maybe you are about to embark on your final year in school and are worried about completing the requirements to graduate.

In this section are scripts to guide you through the myriad emotions that you might be feeling and help you to bring down the stress as you prepare to face the real world. Good luck out there.

Meeting and Completing the Requirements to Graduate

Your final year of college has arrived. Now, all that you must do is make it through your final upper level classes and keep your grades where they need to be. You have to do this and apply for jobs as you prepare to enter the real world after college. If you are feeling stressed as you gear up for meeting your final graduation requirements, try tapping through the following script.

Start with a deep breath and determine how you are feeling. Rate your level of distress and identify any physical sensations associated with your emotions. Now it is time to tap.

1. **Because:** I have so many tough classes this year and I cannot afford to mess up and let my GPA slip because it will ruin my future
2. **Emotion:** Panicked, stressed
3. **Sensation:** Clenched teeth and pain in jaw
4. **Distress:** 0-10________

KC: Even though I am feeling panicked, because I have so many tough classes this year and I have to do well…I cannot afford to mess up and let my GPA slip or it will ruin my future, **I accept my feelings.**

KC: Even though I am stressed because I have so many tough classes and I cannot afford to mess up and ruin my GPA, and my jaw is so painful because I clench my teeth because of all this stress, **I accept myself and my feelings**.

KC: Even though I am so panicked, so stressed, because it's my last year of college and I have so many difficult classes, I can't afford to mess up…ruin my future…and I keep clenching my teeth, **I accept myself and how I feel**.

EB: I feel panicked
SE: It's the last year of college and I have so much to do
UE: So many difficult classes to complete
UN: I have to do well
CP: And it is very stressful
CB: I can't afford to get a bad grade…ruin my GPA
UA: A bad grade could ruin my future
TH: I feel stressed and panicked
EB: There is so much pressure on me this year
SE: What if I screw it up…get a bad grade?
UE: All this stress makes me clench my jaw
UN: I feel this stress in my jaw, it really hurts

CP: I have all this pressure to do well
CB: And the classes are so hard, really challenging
UA: All this pressure…all this stress
TH: It has me panicked
EB: Just one more year and I'm done
SE: I can't afford to ruin my future with a bad grade
UE: There's all this pressure to do well, keep my grades
UN: Not ruin my GPA
CP: I feel the stress in my jaw, my clenched teeth
CB: So panicky about this year, my classes, my grades
UA: One more year to go, but it is such an important year
TH: I feel the stress of it, all the panic, it's in my jaw, the stress and the pain

Continue tapping until the stress, the panic, or other emotion, releases to a 2 or below. Then try the next round for a little positive encouragement.

EB: I've had all this stress
SE: But it feels better now
UE: And I am open to letting some of this stress go
UN: To relaxing the panic
CP: To relaxing my jaw
CB: I am open to trusting myself and my process
UA: And to remembering that I have made it through college so far
TH: I've made it through each previous year
EB: I am open to knowing that I can make it through this year as well
SE: I am open to allowing it to be easier
UE: I am open to less stress and panic
UN: And I am open to more balance, ease and calm
CP: I remind my jaw to release and relax, my teeth to unclench
CB: I am allowing this year to be easier, balanced, calm

UA: I am allowing my jaw to relax, my teeth to unclench
TH: I choose this ease, this peace, this calm now and for this final year of college

Rate your distress level and if it is a 2 or below, try saying the final line of the script as you tap through all the points, to end on a positive note.

Optional Because: I hate my classes; I have to bring my low GPA up; I have a thesis to finish; I have an important presentation or performance; My final exams will be more difficult; I just want to enjoy my last year at college but there is so much to do; I have the hardest classes this year; I am so ready to be done; There are too many things to finish and not enough time

There are more scripts in other sections of the book if you want to tap further on these issues. Check the Table of Contents for the corresponding page numbers.

Optional Emotions: Tension; Feeling overwhelmed; Chronic worry; Fear; Sadness; Anxious feelings; Feeling alone or isolated; Distressed; Unhappy

I Missed a Requirement to Graduate

You've worked hard at university. You've gone to class, completed assignments, and written papers. You've ticked the boxes, checked and double checked and you know that you are on target to walk across that stage at graduation. And wham, out of nowhere, there's one more thing you have to do and haven't. One more class to take, just three more hours to finalize. The problem is, you're full up. There's nowhere to put another class. How could you have missed this tiny thing that could potentially ruin your senior year?

If you find yourself in this predicament, use the following script to release some of the stress. Then you can calmly decide how to best remedy the situation. Begin with a deep inhale and a long, slow exhale. Allow yourself to feel all of your emotions when you think of your missing requirement. Rate your level of distress. Determine if you have any physical sensations related to your emotional state. Now it is time to tap.

1. **Because:** I missed a requirement/class necessary for graduation and now I have to fit it into my schedule
2. **Emotion:** Frustration and panic
3. **Sensation:** Tightness in chest
4. **Distress:** 0-10 ______

KC: Even though I am feeling frustrated because I missed a requirement for graduation and now I have to fit it into my schedule...I don't have room for it...I don't even know how this happened, **I accept myself and my feelings.**

KC: Even though I am panicking because I missed a requirement for graduation and I have to add it into my schedule this year but I don't have the time or the space for the class and I am panicked and my chest is tight, **I accept myself and how I feel**.

KC: Even though I am frustrated and feeling panicked because I missed a requirement for graduation...I have to fit this class into my schedule...I don't have a choice, and I am so panicky that my chest is tight, **I accept myself and how I feel**.

EB: I am panicked
SE: I totally missed a requirement for graduation
UE: I don't know what happened
UN: But I missed it
CP: I have to have this requirement before I can graduate

CB: All this work could be ruined
UA: I might not graduate
TH: If I don't get this requirement in
EB: I have to get it in…I have no choice
SE: Have to complete this requirement and graduate
UE: But where do I put it?
UN: I feel so frustrated and so panicked
CP: My chest is tight, full of panic
CB: My schedule is already full
UA: All this frustration
TH: All this panic is making my chest tight
EB: I have to fit in this requirement but I already have a full schedule
SE: I am panicked…how do I get this done?
UE: Meet this requirement
UN: All this panic, making my chest tight
CP: How can I get it done?
CB: I'm frustrated because I don't know how I missed this
UA: All this panic and frustration
TH: How do I fulfill this requirement so I can graduate?

Tap the emotions down to a 2 or below and then turn it around, using the following script to add in a few positive affirmations supporting you and your ability to solve this problem and meet your requirements.

EB: This panic isn't helping me find an answer
SE: It's only making things worse
UE: I am open to releasing the panic and frustration
UN: Open to finding a way to solve this problem
CP: Open to finding the support I need to figure out a solution
CB: I have worked so hard to graduate
UA: I won't give up…let panic control me
TH: I am open to finding a solution so I can graduate

Take a deep breath and notice how you are feeling. Continue tapping through the script until your distress level has dropped to a 2 or below. You may choose to tap one final round saying the last line on each tapping point. This is a positive way to end your tapping session.

Optional Because: My advisor screwed up and missed this requirement; My advisor is not helpful in this situation; I cannot get into the class I need; My parents are angry; I can't tell my parents; This is a nightmare my last year of college; I may have to stay an extra semester or for the summer; It will cost more money to fix this; What if I can't graduate; All that work for nothing

Optional Emotions: Fear; Anxious feelings; Anger; Tension; Feeling Overwhelmed; Irritated; Pissed off; Stuck; Isolated; Alone; Ruined

Finding an Internship or Job

At some point during college, you will probably apply for an internship or a job. This can be nerve-wracking, especially if you've never done it before. Use this script to help with the nerves and other feelings that come up when you are searching for an internship or a job.

Take a deep breath and focus on the emotions and physical feelings you are experiencing at the moment. Think about what thoughts are triggering these feelings.

1. **Because:** I don't know how to find a job/internship
2. **Emotions:** Nervous, Feeling Overwhelmed, Stressed
3. **Sensations:** Butterflies in my stomach
4. **Distress:** 0-10 ________

KC: Even though I am nervous and stressed because I don't know how to find an internship/job, **I accept myself**.

KC: Even though I don't even know where to start and I'm really nervous and feeling overwhelmed, I **accept myself and my feelings**.

KC: Even though I get so nervous just thinking about finding an internship/job, **I accept myself**.

EB: I don't know how to find an internship/job
SE: I don't even know where to start
UE: I get so nervous thinking about it
UN: I need help with this
CP: Career Counseling isn't helping me and I don't know how to do this by myself
CB: I've never done this before
UA: I'm so nervous…I have butterflies in my stomach
TH: I don't know how to find an internship/job and I'm so nervous
EB: I don't know where to start
SE: What if I do it wrong?
UE: What if I can't find one?
UN: What if I don't like it?
CP: What if it's hard?
CB: All this stress is overwhelming…it's exhausting me
UA: All this stress about finding an internship/job
TH: I'm so nervous about it

Take a deep breath in and think about your intensity. Did anything pop into your head while you were tapping? Don't ignore it because it could be important. Try adding that thought to your tapping routine. Keep adding thoughts, emotions and physical sensations as you continue tapping until you reduce your intensity rating.

Optional Because: I'm scared to look for an internship; I don't want to do an internship; There's so much pressure to pick something useful; There aren't any internships available for my major; I am scared to look for a job; I haven't been able to locate any jobs that I want to do; There is nothing available in my major field that I want to do; I don't want a job in my major because I don't like my major; I don't want a dreary nine to five job; I am not ready to be in the real world; I don't want to do this

Optional Emotions: Fear; Confusion; Feeling Uneasy; Angry; Distraught; Frustrated; Feeling Dread; Stuck; Terrified

The Interview

Here is a script to use when you have an interview for your internship or job. Take a deep inhale and a slow exhale. What emotions are you feeling? Do you notice any physical sensations? Is your belly fluttering? Are your shoulders tight? Change the wording to fit what you are experiencing.

1. **Because:** I have an interview...I have to write a resume...I have no idea what I'm doing
2. **Emotions:** Terrified and nervous; doubting self
3. **Sensations:** Tightness in chest
4. **Distress:** 0-10 _______

KC: Even though I have an interview and I'm so nervous, **I accept myself**.

KC: Even though I am terrified because I have this interview and I have to write a resume...I have no idea what I'm doing, **I accept myself**.

KC: Even though I have this interview, have to write this resume, and I am terrified…I feel all this tightness in my chest, **I accept myself**.

EB: I have an interview
SE: What if I say the wrong thing?
UE: I don't even have a resume
UN: What the heck do I put on a resume
CP: What am I going to say at the interview?
CB: What if they don't like me?
UA: How can I prepare for this…I'm so nervous
TH: I feel it in my chest
EB: I have no idea what I'm doing
SE: Career Counseling isn't helpful
UE: I am sure I'm going to say the wrong thing in the interview and they won't like me
UN: What if I don't get the job/internship?
CP: I'm going to screw this up because I've never done this before
CB: I'm so nervous…I feel tightness in my chest
UA: All this emotion about this interview
TH: What if I screw up?

Take a nice deep inhalation. Continue tapping until you reduce your distress level to a 2. Then move on to the next round.

EB: I'm so nervous…I've never done this before
SE: How do other people do this?
UE: I'm terrified
UN: Others can do this, so why am I so nervous
CP: I'm open to this interview going smoothly and easily
CB: I am open to it going well
UA: I'm open to releasing these nerves
TH: I'm open to having a successful interview

EB: What if I screw up?
SE: But, what if I don't?
UE: I'm going to say the wrong thing...I just know it
UN: I'm going to say all the right things...they'll love me
CP: I'm not going to get this job/internship
CB: I'm totally going to get this internship
UA: What if I screw up this interview or my resume?
TH: I'm doing the best I can and I know I will do well

Take a deep inhalation and slowly exhale. Going back and forth between positive and negative statements can be helpful when you are tapping. Continue tapping until your level of intensity drops and see if you can't get it to a 0. Good luck on your interview! Don't forget to use Hand Tapping before and during your interview to keep your nerves in check.

Optional Because: I stumbled through the last interview; I never know how to answer questions at an interview; I will make a bad impression; I always mess up interviews; I don't have the right clothes for an interview; I don't know if I want this job

Optional Emotions: Frustrated; Scared; Confused; Unsure; Torn; Frantic

I Am Not Ready for the Real World

What happens after the classes end, the dorm room or apartment is emptied, and life on campus, at college, is finished? The frightening and fantastic reality is...it's all up to you. It's called the future or real life, and no one ever claimed it would be easy. But it can be rewarding, fun, an adventure, and even pretty awesome. Whatever challenges you face as you approach the end of your university years, tapping can help cut the stress and open room for new possibilities to appear.

Start with a deep inhale and a long exhale. Tune into your emotions as you think about the real world. Do you notice any physical sensations accompanying these feelings? Rate your distress level and then give the script a try. Good luck out there.

1. **Because:** I am not ready for the real world…to take care of myself
2. **Emotion:** Petrified
3. **Sensation:** I can't sleep
4. **Distress:** 0-10 _______

KC: Even though I am petrified because I am not ready for the real world and I lie awake at night, unable to sleep because I am so scared, **I accept myself and how I feel.**

KC: Even though I am totally petrified because I am about to graduate from college and I am not ready for the real world…for taking care of myself, **I accept myself and how I feel**.

KC: Even though I am completely petrified, because I'm not ready to be on my own and I can't sleep because I'm so scared, I **accept myself and how I feel**.

EB: I am petrified
SE: I'm about to graduate from college and I'm not ready
UE: I'm not ready for the real world
UN: Not ready to take care of myself
CP: I am totally petrified
CB: How do I do this?
UA: Take care of myself all by myself
TH: I can't even sleep at night because I am so scared
EB: I am scared of getting out of college, taking care of myself
SE: I know I'm not ready and I lie awake at night thinking about it, worrying about it

UE: I'm not ready for the real world and it scares me
UN: I am so scared that I can't sleep
CP: I have never been so totally alone before
CB: Totally petrified
UA: I have to take care of myself, alone
TH: I am petrified because I am graduating and I'm not ready for the real world

Take a breath and reassess your emotions. What is your level of distress? When it has dropped to a 2 or below, tap through the next two rounds of more positive statements.

EB: So I'm graduating
SE: Going out there on my own
UE: And it is a new thing, new for me anyway
UN: It feels like I'm not ready
CP: But maybe it's possible that I'm more ready than I think
CB: After all, I've been here, at college, basically on my own
UA: I haven't been at home
TH: I have a job and a place to live
EB: So maybe I'm more ready than I think
SE: I'm open to the idea that I am going to be okay living on my own
UE: On my own in the real world
UN: I'm open to the idea that the real world is not as scary as it seems
CP: I'm open to releasing this fear and allowing myself to be more relaxed about this
CB: I'm almost a college graduate after all. I am ready to do this
UA: I have a degree, skills, a job and a place to live and I'm ready to make this easy
TH: I'm open to releasing the fear and to allowing living in the real world to be easy

Take a deep breath and notice how you are feeling. Continue tapping through the script until your distress level has dropped to a 2 or below. You may choose to tap one final round saying the last line on each tapping point. This is a positive way to end your tapping session.

Optional Because: I can't find a job after graduation; I don't know what I want to do after graduation; I am about to graduate from undergraduate school/law school/medical school and I don't know what to do next; I may not like my job/career; I can't find a job in my field; I might not be able to support myself; I can't find a place to live; I can't find a roommate; My student loans are due and I have to start paying them back; How can I afford to live in the real

There are more scripts in other sections of the book if you want to tap further on these issues. Check the Table of Contents for the corresponding page numbers.

Optional Emotions: Stressed; Overwhelmed; Panicked; Tense; Isolated; Rejected; Alone; Anxious; Worried; Insecure

Section Nine
Miscellaneous Scripts

In this section, you will find general tapping scripts about other issues you may have at school. Remember to substitute the words and emotions that best fit your particular situation.

What's the Point of College?

Not everyone loves the college experience. Some students want to finish their college career and move into real life. For them, college is a necessity, and one they would forego if they could. Required general education classes seem pointless, a bunch of extra work with no end benefit. If you are one of the students who wants college over as quickly as possible, try the following script.

1. **Because:** Most of college is a waste of time…I'd leave but I need a degree
2. **Emotion:** Frustration and anger
3. **Sensation:** Shoulder tension
4. **Distress:** 0-10 ________

KC: Even though I am angry and my shoulders are tense because most of college is a waste of my time and I want it over with as soon as possible, **I accept myself**.

KC: Even though I am frustrated that I have to be in college, taking general education classes, wasting my time…my shoulders are tense and painful, **I accept myself and how I feel**.

KC: Even though I hate being at college because I don't see the point...it is a waste of time and I wouldn't be here if I didn't need a degree, **I accept myself and how I feel.**

EB: I hate being in college...it's a waste of time
SE: My shoulders tense up thinking about it...
UE: If I didn't need a college degree, I'd leave now
UN: The general education requirements don't apply to what I want to do
CP: But I still have to waste my time taking them
CB: And I honestly don't see why
UA: I get so frustrated when I think about all the time I've spent here
TH: Time spent on classes I don't need
EB: What a waste
SE: I'd rather be in the real world, working
UE: But I have to get a degree to get the job I want in the real world
UN: So I have to take these ridiculous classes and that makes me angry
CP: I feel like I'm trapped
CB: I'm so frustrated...angry...my shoulders are painful and tense
UA: What's the point of all these classes that don't apply to my life?
TH: I want to work, to get out into the real world, not waste any more time here
EB: I want to get this over with as soon as possible
SE: I wonder if it would go more quickly if I let go of the anger and frustration
UE: After all, I do have to be here, whether I love it or not
UN: Maybe I can make the best of it...
CP: There are some good parts...like my friendships

CB: And I have learned something from most classes, even the ones I didn't want to take

UA: I'm open to the possibility that I can make this easier, even enjoy parts of it

TH: I'm open to releasing the anger and frustration around college...to allowing myself to get the most I can out of the experience

Tap on the script for one round or more then pause, noticing if any new emotions or physical sensations surface. Continue tapping until your distress level lowers to a 2 or below, then try tapping all the points while saying the last two lines. This allows you to end your tapping on a positive note.

Optional Because: Why do I have to get a degree for what I want to do; Why can't I take the classes that meet my degree requirements and be done; None of my friends feel this way...what is wrong with me

Optional Emotions: Desperation; Sadness; Bored; Exhausted

Transportation

Getting around off campus can really pose a problem, especially if you don't have a car. If you have a job or an appointment it isn't always easy to find a means to get where you need to go. What do you do if you've run out of toothpaste or deodorant or a prescription that you have to take on a regular schedule? Use this script if you have issues getting around. After all, you do not need another source of stress.

Begin with a deep breath in and think about your emotional and physical feelings surrounding your transportation problems.

1. **Because:** I have to go places and I don't have a car…I can't afford it…I'm always late
2. **Emotions:** frustration, stress
3. **Sensations:** (Include if you feel any physical sensations related to your emotions)
4. **Distress:** 0-10 ________

KC: Even though I am so frustrated because I have to go places and I don't have a car, **I accept myself and the situation**.

KC: Even though this situation is adding to all my stress, **I accept myself**.

KC: Even though I'm always asking for rides and always late because I don't have a car, **I accept myself**.

EB: I need a car on campus but I can't afford it
SE: No one will help me out with a ride
UE: I always need to ask my friends for rides and it's so frustrating
UN: I can never get where I need to go
CP: Campus transportation sucks…it takes so long and I'm always late
CB: It's so frustrating
UA: I need a car
TH: It's so frustrating that I don't have a car on campus…I can't afford one…
EB: I hate this!
SE: I want to be able to go places when I want to and need to
UE: I'm so frustrated…I hate asking for rides all the time
UN: AAHH…this is so frustrating
CP: I need a car
CB: I get so frustrated when I'm always late because I have to find a ride

UA: This is so frustrating
TH: I am so frustrated because I can't afford a car and I really need a car at college

Take a deep breath. Recheck your distress level. Did anything pop into your head while you were tapping? Try adding that as you tap through again.

Optional Because: I can't afford to have a car on campus; My parents won't let me have a car; My parents cannot afford to get me a car for college; Public transportation is not reliable; Campus is too big to walk everywhere; I have to drive to run my errands; There is no place within walking distance to run my errands; I am stuck on campus without a car; I don't know anyone with a car who can give me a ride; My friends have different schedules and can't give me a ride; I am the only person I know without a car

There are more scripts in other sections of the book if you want to tap further on these issues. Check the Table of Contents for the corresponding page numbers.

Optional Emotions: Angry; Irritated; Envious; Disappointed; Stuck; Dissatisfied; Miserable

Greek Life

Many campuses have extensive fraternity and sorority communities. Greek life can offer students social and philanthropic opportunities. This involvement can be fun and a helpful resume builder. Greek organizations are also notorious for parties, hazing and peer pressure, all of which can add equal measures of fun and stress to your college experience. Use the script below if you are struggling with any aspect of Greek life. Change the wording to fit your situation. Using your own words is always the best way to release the emotions surrounding your current situation.

Begin with a deep breath in. What emotions are you feeling? Do you notice any physical sensations accompanying your emotions? Rate your level of distress and begin tapping.

1. **Because:** I know I won't get a bid
2. **Emotions:** Apprehensive, unsure, and scared
3. **Sensations:** Queasy stomach
4. **Distress:** 0-10 ________

KC: Even though I am scared and apprehensive because I know I won't get a bid from the sorority I want, and my stomach feels queasy thinking about it, **I accept myself**. (repeat 3 times)

EB: I am so scared
SE: Because I am afraid I won't get a bid
UE: There is one sorority I want a bid from
UN: But what if I don't get a bid from them?
CP: What if I don't get a bid at all?
CB: I am so apprehensive, waiting to find out…my stomach is queasy
UA: All this fear and apprehension
TH: What if I don't get a bid from the sorority I want?

Take a long, deep breath. Repeat this script, using wording that fits your situation or the wording we have provided until your Distress level has reduced. Making the tapping personal and specific allows for a better release of the distress.

Optional Because: I don't know if I should pledge; I didn't get a bid; I got a bid but it wasn't the organization I wanted; I got more than one bid and I don't know which one to choose; Rushing and pledging take so much time away from everything else I need to do; I pledged but now I hate it; I feel pressured to party; I am being hazed; The pledging requirements are ridiculous; I can't believe I am doing this; I want to drop out of pledging but I don't know if I can; None of my friends will understand or like me if I drop out of pledging; Pledging is stupid

There are more scripts in other sections of the book if you want to tap further on these issues. Check the Table of Contents for the corresponding page numbers.

Optional Emotions: Worried; Rejected; Overwhelmed; Helpless; Nervous; Pressured; Angry; Trapped; Alarmed; Victimized

I Am GLBT or Questioning

If you are questioning your sexuality or if you are worried about sharing your sexuality with friends or family, use the following script. Your sexuality is a very important and personal part of who you are. To fully embrace all of yourself it's important to share this part of you with those to whom you are closest. If you notice any physical sensations, voice what you are feeling as you tap.

1. **Because:** I know I am gay but I don't know how to share it with others
2. **Emotion:** Fear and stress
3. **Sensation:** (Include if you feel any physical sensations related to your emotions)
4. **Distress:** 0-10 ________

KC: Even though I am stressed and afraid because I don't know how to share my sexuality with my friends and family…I know that I am gay but I don't know how to tell them, **I accept myself**.

KC: Even though I am stressed because I am tired of not being true to myself, of not fully embracing my life and my identity, and that includes my sexuality, but it's scary to share with my friends and family that I am gay…what if they reject me and can't handle what I tell them, **I accept myself**.

KC: Even though I am stressed and scared, because I'm gay but I don't know how to share my sexuality with my friends and family…I'm afraid they can't handle it and might reject me, **I accept myself just as I am**.

EB: I'm so scared and stressed
SE: I'm gay but I haven't told my friends or my family
UE: And I'm scared to tell them about this part of me
UN: About my sexuality
CP: It's such an important part of who I am
CB: I can't live a lie any longer, can't keep it from the people I care about
UA: But what if they reject me because I'm gay?
TH: What if they can't handle it when I tell them?
EB: I'm so scared
SE: So afraid to lose the people I love
UE: But I'm also afraid to hide myself, to not be true to me
UN: I have to express who I am, to tell my friends and family
CP: But I'm still scared…so stressed
CB: What if they reject me for being me
UA: But, what if they accept me for who I am?
TH: I'm open to sharing my sexuality and being accepted for who I am

As you tap, add whatever comes to you. Make the script your own. Once you've completed a few rounds of tapping, stop and take a deep breath. Notice if your emotions or your physical sensations have changed. Add in new emotions or sensations to subsequent tapping rounds. Continue until your distress has dropped to a 2 or below. As a final round, tap on each point while saying the last line, to finish on a positive note. Return to this script, or to your version, as often as you need until you are ready to share who you are with those you love.

Optional Because: I am questioning my sexuality; I am having issues with someone else's sexuality

Optional Emotions: Alone; Frightened; Angry; Insecure; Uncertain; Worried

Study Abroad

An exciting option at college is the opportunity to study abroad. If you are considering a stint overseas, you're undoubtedly experiencing a few emotions. Maybe you are worried about being homesick; perhaps funds are an issue. Use the following script if you are planning to study overseas. Personalize your tapping using the Optional Because phrases and Optional Emotions or fill in with your own choices if we haven't covered your situation. Start with a deep breath in and a long breath out. Remember to check back in and substitute other phrasing options as your emotions shift. Get to tapping and enjoy your time in a land far away.

1. **Because:** I want to study abroad but I don't know where to go
2. **Emotions:** I feel confused
3. **Sensations:** (Include if you feel any physical sensations related to your emotions)
4. **Distress:** 0-10 __________

KC: Even though I am confused because I want to study abroad but I don't know where to go, **I accept myself and my feelings**.

KC: Even though I want to study abroad but it is so hard…so confusing to decide where to go, **I accept myself**.

KC: Even though I really don't know what to do…I am feeling so confused because I want to study abroad but I don't know where to go, **I accept myself**.

EB: I am feeling so confused
SE: I don't know what to do
UE: I really want to study overseas but I don't know where to go
UN: I wish this wasn't so difficult
CP: It really is hard to choose from all the options
CB: Why am I so stressed about studying abroad?
UA: I wish I wasn't but I don't know what to do
TH: I am so confused because I don't know where to study overseas

Take a breath. Do you notice any physical sensations when you think about studying abroad? Go through the script again adding any new emotions or physical feelings. Repeat and modify until you have reduced your distress level.

Optional Because: I want to study abroad, but my parents won't let me; I want to study abroad but I can't afford it; I don't know how to make study abroad work with my major; My degree requires I study abroad but I don't want to; I'm scared I'll miss my family/friends; I'm scared I won't know anyone there; I'm scared of the language barrier.

There are more scripts in other sections of the book if you want to tap further on these issues. Check the Table of Contents for the corresponding page numbers.

Optional Emotions: Fear; Anxiousness; Frustration; Irritation; Uneasy; Tension; Worried; Stressed

To Transfer or to Stay

Sometimes the school you have chosen turns out to be a bad fit and you consider transferring to a different college. If you think you want to transfer but you are feeling stressed about making the decision, try this script.

Begin with a deep breath in and a long breath out. Allow your mind to think of all the things about your current school that you don't like and why you might want to transfer. Think about any questions or worries you have about transferring to a new school. Rate your distress level and remember to change any wording that doesn't fit your needs to make it as specific to you as possible.

1. **Because:** I don't like it here and I think I want to transfer
2. **Emotions:** Worry and confusion
3. **Sensations:** Nervous belly
4. **Distress:** 0-10 ________

KC: Even though I don't like this school and I think I might want to transfer, **I accept myself and my feelings**.

KC: Even though I am confused because I think I want to transfer...thinking about staying upsets me, but the thought of transferring gives me a nervous belly and I don't know what to do, **I accept myself.**

KC: Even though I am confused and worried about whether I should transfer and what it would entail, **I accept myself.**

EB: I don't like it here and I think I want to transfer
SE: I don't know what to do
UE: All this confusion and worry…I feel it in my belly
UN: I'm confused about whether I should just suck it up and stay or move to a new school
CP: I'm worried if I leave I might not like my new school either
CB: I would have to make all new friends and learn a new campus all over again
UA: I just don't know what to do…I'm so confused!
TH: I think I want to transfer but just thinking about it gives me a nervous belly
EB: What if I don't like my new school either?
SE: What if my credits don't transfer
UE: I'll have to make all new friends and figure out the campus
UN: I'm so confused and so worried about making this decision
CP: I don't know what to do!
CB: What if I make the wrong choice?
UA: I think I want to transfer
TH: But I'm so confused and so worried…I don't know what to do

Take a deep breath in and release it. Check in with the sensations and emotions you are feeling. Have the sensations shifted to a new place in your body? Have your emotions changed? Take note of these changes and fit them into the script and tap another round or two. Keep rechecking your emotions and sensations in your body and tap through them all until you have a clearer mind. Consider tapping through the reasons you want to leave your current school and then reassess whether or not you still want to transfer. This will help you with your decision making.

Did I Make the Wrong Choice to Transfer?

If you decided to transfer but are now having doubts, try this script. There are lots of different emotions that go along with change. Acknowledge these emotions and any sensations you are feeling in your body about the changes that are coming. Begin with a long, deep breath. Rate your distress level and begin tapping.

1. **Because:** I decided to transfer but now I'm not so sure… I'm sad to leave my friends and I might not like my new school
2. **Emotions:** Sadness, worry, confusion, feeling torn
3. **Sensations:** upset stomach
4. **Distress:** 0-10 _______

KC: Even though I feel so confused and sad because I decided to transfer but now I'm not sure I want to leave this school, **I accept myself, the decisions I made and all these feelings**.

KC: Even though I made a choice and now I'm not sure it was the right one…I'm torn because part of me wants to stay…not transfer, I **accept myself and all I'm feeling**.

KC: Even though I made this decision and now I'm questioning it…there is so much to think about and I'm worried that I made the wrong choice, **I accept myself.**

EB: I made a decision to transfer and now I think I want to stay

SE: I'm going to miss my friends so much and that makes me sad

UE: I'll have to learn a new school all over again…what if I don't like it there?

UN: I'm so worried and confused…so torn

CP: I get an upset stomach just thinking about this…what if I really messed up?
CB: I don't know if I really want to transfer now
UA: I'm so confused and worried that I made the wrong choice
TH: All this worry about transferring…what if I made the wrong choice
EB: I'm going to miss all my friends
SE: What if I can't find new friends at the new school?
UE: What if I don't like the classes or professors at the new school?
UN: All these what-if's…what have I done?
CP: I'm so confused and so torn
CB: I feel all this in my belly, I don't think I made the right choice
UA: What have I done?
TH: I'm worried I made the wrong choice to transfer

Take a breath. What came up for you during that round of tapping? Did you have any other thoughts or concerns? Focus on the emotions and rate the distress level. Continue tapping through the previous script changing the wording to meet the thoughts and emotions that are coming up for you.

Optional Because: Things changed since I made my decision and now I want to stay; I have to add a year to finish my degree because I am transferring; I want to stay at my old school; It is too late to change my decision but I wish I could; I don't know anyone at the new school

Optional Emotions: Panicked; Frustrated; Frightened; Lonely; Terrified

Tapping Is Not Working

Sometimes you might think that tapping isn't working for you. This can exacerbate the emotions you are experiencing which will not help your situation. Here is a script to use when you feel that EFT is not working.

Begin with a deep breath. Assess your emotions and your body sensations and start tapping.

1. **Because:** Tapping isn't working for me
2. **Emotion:** Frustration, anger, annoyance
3. **Sensation:** Headache
4. **Distress:** 0-10 _______

KC: Even though tapping isn't working for me and I am getting really frustrated, **I accept myself.**

KC: Even though I am getting get no relief from tapping and I am becoming very annoyed with it, **I accept myself.**

KC: Even though tapping on my face and body seems ridiculous and it's giving me a headache, **I accept myself.**

EB: Tapping isn't working for me
SE: I am so annoyed and frustrated right now
UE: I am getting such a headache trying to get this to work
UN: But tapping isn't working for me
CP: This is so annoying and frustrating
CB: I look ridiculous when I try tapping and it isn't even working
UA: Honestly, how is this supposed to help me?
TH: Tapping isn't working for me...nothing seems to fix all the stress I have in my life

EB: This is so ridiculous
SE: It isn't working
UE: I'm so frustrated with tapping…I'm getting a headache
UN: Tapping isn't working for me and I'm so annoyed
CP: I need to figure out how to release this stress I have and tapping isn't helping
CB: Tapping isn't working for me…it's just making me more frustrated and annoyed
UA: I want to be open to this working, I really do
TH: But tapping isn't doing anything except adding to my frustration and giving me a headache

Continue tapping and venting until your distress rating has reduced. Think about why you might not want tapping to work. Why don't you want to release the issue at hand? Does keeping the issue in some way benefit you? If you can think of reasons why you might want to hold onto the problem you are trying to release, tap about that. Often, our subconscious mind prevents us from going too deeply into an issue or problem as a way to protect us. If this is the case, EFT might not be working as effectively as it could. If you find tapping on a subject isn't working, try examining why you might not want to release those emotions.

Appendix A
The Tapping Points

Basic Recipe

KC – Karate Chop
EB – Eyebrow
SE – Side of eye
UE – Under eye
UN – Under nose
CP – Chin Point
CB – Collarbone
UA – Under arm
TH – Top of Head

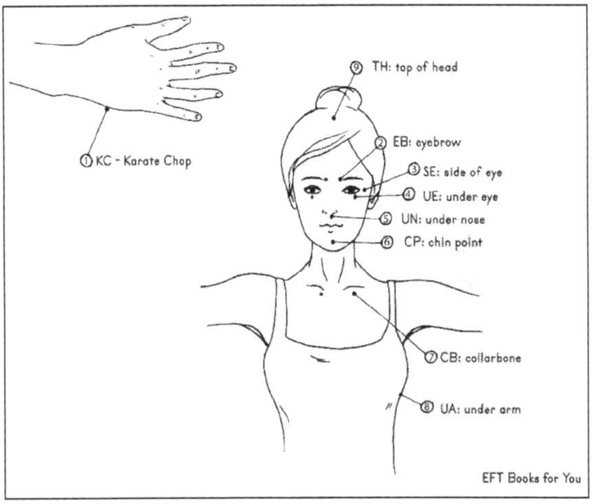

Hand Points

KC – Karate Chop
TH – Thumb
IF – Index Finger
MF – Middle Finger
LF – Little Finger
GP – Gamut Point

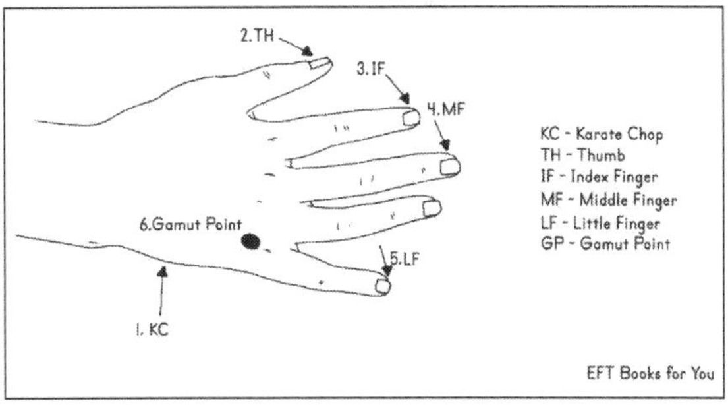

Visit our website, www.eftbooksforyou.com/2017straightA for tapping demonstrations using the Basic Recipe and the Hand Points.

Appendix B
Sample Scripts

In this appendix, you will find several sample scripts. The **Because**, **Emotions** and **Sensations** have not been filled in. Change the words when you need to so that the scripts make sense. We are only providing suggestions, not concrete forms that must be followed. Before you begin, take time to sit quietly, breathe deeply, and tune inward, allowing yourself to feel, sense or visualize the perfect words to fill in your personal script. As always, determine your level of **Distress** before you begin tapping.

Use these scripts as templates for your own EFT tapping sessions. As you work with these examples, filling in with the details specific to you, you will discover that tapping is not a strict system that has to be followed perfectly. You can deviate in the order of your because and emotions, add in the physical sensations where you wish and generally make your tapping your personal experience. Remember, there is no right or wrong way to tap. Now it's time to start Tapping It Out!

Blank Script

This is your script to fill in as you wish. Be specific. You can use examples from this appendix or other parts of the book if you are unsure about what to do. Remember, it is not as much what you say as the fact that you are saying it that makes the difference. As you tap make the experience what you need it to be. Rant, vent, express your rage, your humiliation or sadness, whatever the emotion. Use your language. Yell, even swear, if you need to. Be sure, however, to do this when you are alone and to respect the other people living near you or in your vicinity.

1. **Because**: List here ______________________________
2. **Emotions**: Tune in and write down how you are feeling: ______________________________
3. **Sensations:** Include if you feel any physical sensations related to your emotions: ______________________________
4. **Distress:** 0-10: ________

Set-up Statement: Tap on the **Karate Chop (KC)** three times using your set-up starting with **"Even though"** and ending with a statement of acceptance, such as **"I accept myself"**.

KC: Even though *(fill in emotion)* because *(fill in because)* **I accept myself and my feelings**. (3x)

Reminder Phrase: Say this phrase or variations of your **Because, Emotions**, and **Sensations** while taping on the **Basic Recipe** or the **Hand Points** (see appendix A for diagrams)

Basic Recipe: Tap on the basic recipe points until you reduce your distress. Follow the suggestions or be more specific. Use your words.

EB: I am *(fill in emotion)*
SE: Because *(fill in because)*
UE: I'm really *(fill in emotion)* and I feel *(fill in sensation)* when I think about it
UN: All this *(fill in emotion)* because *(fill in because)*
CP: I am so *(fill in emotion)*...
CB: It makes me feel *(fill in sensation)* just thinking about it

UA: I can't stop thinking about this…it makes me so *(fill in emotion)*…makes me feel *(fill in sensation)* in my body
TH: I'm so *(fill in emotion)* that I feel *(fill in sensation)*, because *(fill in because)*…

Below are some sample scripts based on ones found in different sections of the book. We've taken out the specific words so you can fill in the blanks with the words that work best for you

College is So Expensive

Optional Because: Paying for college is hard because tuition is so expensive; I have to meet scholarship requirements; I have to meet financial aid requirements; I have to pay back loans after I graduate; I didn't get any scholarships or qualify for financial aid; Paying for college is hard for my parents; I have to pay for books; I have so many other expenses; Maybe I should get a job; I don't think I can handle a job and school; I have a job and I don't know how I will manage; I need to learn to budget and I don't know how; I've never managed money before

Optional Emotions: Guilt; Fear; Anxiousness; Overwhelm; Stress; Confusion

Optional Sensations: Shoulder Pain; Headache; Racing heart; Stiff neck; Nauseous

1. **Because:** ________________________________
2. **Emotion:** ________________________________
3. **Sensation:** ______________________________
4. **Distress:** 0-10 _______

KC: **Even though** *I am (fill in emotion)* because *(fill in because)*, and I feel *(fill in sensation)* when I think about *(fill in because)*, **I accept myself and how I feel**. (3 times)

EB: I'm *(fill in emotion)* about *(fill in because)*
SE: Because *(fill in because)*
UE: I'm really *(fill in emotion)* and I feel *(fill in sensation)* when I think about it
UN: How am I going to pay for college with tuition as expensive as it is
CP: I am so *(fill in emotion)*…
CB: It's so much money and it makes me *(fill in sensation)* to think about it
UA: I'm *(fill in emotion)* and I feel it in my body, *(fill in sensation)*
TH: I'm so *(fill in emotion)*, I feel *(fill in sensation)*, because *(fill in because)*…

Professor Problems

Optional Because: I do not like my professor; I am having a problem with my professor; I hate my professor; My professor is mean; My professor is arrogant; My professor is an unfair grader; My professor is hard to understand because he/she has an accent; My professor does not explain the material; I am afraid to talk to my professor; My professor's grading system sucks; The lecture class is so big, I am just a number, a nobody to this professor; His/her teaching style does not work with my learning style

Optional Emotions: Angry; Frustrated; Stressed; Irritated; Afraid; Discouraged; Annoyed; Upset; Anxious; Confused; Furious; Embarrassed

Optional Sensations: Headache; Neck pain; Shoulder pain or tightness; Butterflies in stomach; Queasy; Nauseous; Sweaty Palms; Double vision; Tightness in chest; Clenched jaw; Breathless; Hip pain; Back pain; Other joint pain

1. **Because:** ______________________________
2. **Emotions:** ______________________________
3. **Sensations:** ______________________________
4. **Distress:** 0-10 ________

KC: Even though I am feeling *(fill in emotion)* because *(fill in because)*, **I accept myself**.

KC: Even though I/My *(fill in because)*, and I am feeling *(fill in emotion)* and I feel it in my body, *(fill in body sensation)* **I accept myself and my feelings**.

KC: Even though I'm feeling *(fill in emotion)* because *(fill in because)* I **accept myself**.

EB: My professor is so *(fill in because)*
SE: I am feeling *(fill in emotion)*
UE: How am I going to get through their class?
UN: I have such a problem with this professor
CP: (State problem using optional because to help with wording or use your words)
CB: (Repeat)
UA: All this *(fill in emotion)* surrounding this professor because *(fill in because)*
TH: These issues with my professor
EB: *(State the because or problem)*
SE: All this *(fill in emotion)*
UE: I feel it in my body...all this *(fill in sensation)*
UN: I just don't like my professor
CP: *(State problem using your words)*
UA: This problem with my professor
TH: All this *(fill in emotion)* surrounding my professor because (*fill in because)*

I Can't Decide on a Major

Optional Because: I don't know how to pick my major; I don't know what to pick for my major; I'm so confused, there are so many requirements for a major; There are so many requirements, how will I get it all done; How do I find an internship that works for my major; I chose a major, but I don't like it; I have a major, but I want to switch; What if it's too late to switch majors

Optional Emotions: Stressed; Stressed out; Overwhelm/overwhelmed; Confused/confusion; Upset; Anxious/anxiousness; Worry/worried; Upset; Feeling Stuck; Frustration/Frustrated

Optional Sensations: Headache; Neck pain; Shoulder pain or tightness; Butterflies in stomach; Queasy; Nauseous; Sweaty Palms; Double vision; Tightness in chest; Clenched jaw; Breathless; Hip pain; Back pain; Other joint pain

1. **Because:** ______________________________
2. **Emotions:** ______________________________
3. **Sensations:** ______________________________
4. **Distress:** 0-10 ________

KC: Even though I am feeling *(insert emotion)*, because *(insert because)* **I accept myself.**

KC: Even though this is very *(insert emotion)*, because *(insert because)* **I accept myself.**

KC: Even though *(insert because)* and that *(insert emotion)*, **I accept myself and these feelings.**

EB: I am so *(insert emotion)*
SE: Because *(insert because)*
UE: I just don't know what to do

UN: What if I do the wrong thing? What if I mess up?
CP: All this *(insert emotion)* around my major
CB: Because *(insert because)*
UA: I'm really feeling this and it is intense *(state because using different words)*
TH: All this *(insert emotion)* because *(insert trigger)*
EB: What should I do…I just don't know
SE: All this *(insert emotion)*, it is very intense
UE: All this *(insert emotion)* because *(insert trigger)*
UN: I hate not knowing what to do!
CP: And how I am feeling isn't helping me
CB: All this *(insert emotion)* because *(insert trigger)*
UA: I am really feeling this and it is intense
TH: *(insert because)* and I am feeling so *(insert emotion)*

Relationships

Optional Because: My friend and I had a fight; I cannot connect to anyone on campus; My friends are pressuring me to party; My friends are pressuring me to drink; My friends are pressuring me to do drugs; I caused drama with a friend and now I feel guilty; A friend caused drama and I am in the middle of it; My old friendships at home aren't the same anymore; My friends aren't getting along and I feel stuck in the middle; Sometimes I do stupid things to impress my friends; I just don't want to be friends with *(insert name)*; My boyfriend/girlfriend and I broke up; I want to be in a relationship but can't find anyone; I was rejected by someone I like; I miss my boyfriend/girlfriend from home

Optional Emotions: Stressed; Angry; Frustrated; Distressed; Lonely; Sad; Pressured; Stressed; Overwhelmed; Attacked; Trapped; Embarrassed; Mortified; Guilty; Despondent; Ashamed; Rejected; Heartbroken

Optional Sensations: Headache; Neck pain; Shoulder pain or tightness; Butterflies in stomach; Queasy; Nauseous; Sweaty Palms; Double vision; Tightness in chest; Clenched jaw; Breathless; Can't catch breath; Hip pain; Back pain; Other joint pain

1. **Because:** ______________________________
2. **Emotions:** ______________________________
3. **Sensations:** ______________________________
4. **Distress:** 0-10 ________

KC: Even though *(fill in because)*, **and** I feel *(fill in emotion)*, **I accept myself.**

KC: Even though I am feeling *(fill in emotion)* because *(fill in because)* **I accept myself.**

KC: Even though *(fill in because)* and I feel *(fill in emotion)*, I feel it in my body *(fill in body sensation)* **I accept myself and how I feel.**

EB: *(Insert because)*
SE: And I feel *(insert emotion)*
UE: I don't know what to do
UN: Because *(insert because)*
CP: All this *(insert emotion)*
CB: Because *(insert because)*
UA: I feel so *(insert emotion)*
TH: This issue with *(insert name of person of applicable)*
EB: Because *(insert because)*
SE: I just don't know what to do, I feel so *(insert emotion)*
UE: What should I do?
UN: *(Insert because)*
CP: I really don't know what to do *(state because in different words being specific)*
CB: All this *(insert emotion)*

UA: *(Insert because)*

TH: I feel so *(insert emotion)* because *(insert because including name of person if applicable)*

Appendix C
Resources

Books

The Tapping Solution: A Revolutionary System for Stress-Free Living
By Nick Ortner

The Tapping Solution for Weight Loss & Body Confidence: A Woman's Guide to Stressing Less, Weighing Less, and Loving More
By Jessica Ortner

The EFT Manual
By Dawson Church

EFT for Weight Loss
By Dawson Church

Online

Substance Abuse

College Campus Addiction Resource Guidebook:
www.learnpsychology.org/college-campus-addiction-resources/

Eating Disorders

Overeaters Anonymous
https://oa.org/

Eating Disorder Hope
www.eatingdisorderhope.com

Suicide

Suicide Prevention Lifeline
www.suicidepreventionlifeline.org

Sexual Assault

Rape, Abuse & Incest National Network
www.RAINN.org

Dating Abuse

Abusive Relationship
http://www.loveisrespect.org/

The National Domestic Violence Hotline
http://www.thehotline.org/is-this-abuse/

Depression

Anxiety and Depression Association of America
http://www.adaa.org/living-with-anxiety/college-students/find-help

Student Guide to Surviving Stress and Anxiety in College & Beyond
http://www.learnpsychology.org/student-stress-anxiety-guide/

Depression and Bipolar Support Alliance
www.dbsalliance.org

Phone Numbers/Hotlines

Substance Abuse:

1-800-662-HELP (4357)

Eating Disorder:
1-800-931-2237

Suicide:
1-800-273-8255

Sexual Assault:
1-800-656-4673

Dating Abuse:
1-866-331-9474

Depression:
1-800-826-3632

Gay & Lesbian Hotline:
1-888-THE-GLNH (843-4564)

Find Us

For more information and tapping demonstrations, visit the following sites.

Website Address:
www.EFTBooksforYou.com

On Facebook:
www.Facebook.com/TappedoutEFTBooks

On Instagram:
EFTBooksforYou

Our Individual Practice Websites

Becki Stevens
www.RebeccaStevensCoaching.com

Kelley Pryor Amrein
www.SpiritGuidedJourneys.com

Endnotes

1 "The Chinese Medicine Meridian System | Academy of Classical Oriental Sciences." Academy of Classical Oriental Sciences. http://www.acos.org/articles/the-chinese-medicine-meridian-system/ (Accessed August 03, 2016).

2 Charles A. Moss, *Power of the Five Elements: The Chinese Medicine Path to Healthy Aging and Stress Resistance* (Berkeley: North Atlantic Books, 2010), 33.

3 Gary Craig, *The EFT Manual* (Santa Rosa, CA: Energy Psychology Press, 2008), 17, February 2008) http://taisa.si/wp/wp-content/uploads/2014/03/EFT-Manual.pdf_ (Accessed July 12, 2016).

4 "Understanding the Stress Response," Harvard Health Publications, http://www.health.harvard.edu/staying-healthy/understanding-the-stress-response_(Accessed September 6, 2016).

5 "Your Amazing Brain," http://www.youramazingbrain.org/brainchanges/stressbrain.htm_(Accessed September 6, 2016).

6 Michael Randall, "The Physiology of Stress: Cortisol and the Hypothalamic-Pituitary-Adrenal Axis," http://dujs.dartmouth.edu/2011/02/the-physiology-of-stress-cortisol-and-the-hypothalamic-pituitary-adrenal-axis/#.V88xLZgrI2w (Accessed September 6, 2016).

7 Dawson Church, *The EFT Manual* (Fulton, CA: Energy Psychology Press, 2013), 73-74.

8 Dawson Church, Midanelle A. De Asis, and Audry J. Brooks, "Brief Group Intervention Using Emotional Freedom Techniques for Depression in College Students: A Randomized Controlled Trial," https://www.hindawi.com/journals/drt/2012/257172/ (Accessed July 12, 2016).

9 Louis Fox, "Is Acupoint Tapping an Active Ingredient or an Inert Placebo in Emotional Freedom Techniques (EFT)? A Randomized Controlled Dismantling Study," Energy Psychology Journal, http://energypsychologyjournal.org/is-acupoint-tapping-an-active-ingredient-or-an-inert-placebo-in-emotional-freedom-techniques-eft-a-randomized-controlled-dismantling-study/, (Accessed July 12, 2016).

10 Dawson Church, *The EFT Manual* (Fulton, CA: Energy Psychology Press, 2013), 82.

11 Church, 89.

12 Church, 90.

13 Mel Pohl, MD, FASAM, "Five Surprising Lessons I've Learned about Chronic Pain," Phycology Today, July 30, 2012, https://www.psychologytoday.com/blog/day-without-pain/201207/5-surprising-lessons-i-ve-learned-about-chronic-pain?collection=125783, (Accessed October 22, 2016).

14 Victoria Tennant, "The Powerful Impact of Stress," Johns Hopkins School of Education, http://education.jhu.edu/PD/newhorizons/strategies/topics/Keeping%20Fit%20for%20Learning/stress.html, (Accessed September 7, 2016).

15 "Test Anxiety," American Test Anxiety Association, http://amtaa.org/ (Accessed September 7, 2016).

16 Bruce Lipton, Ph.D., *The Honeymoon Effect: The Science of Creating Heaven on Earth* (Carlsbad, CA: Hay House, 2013), 50.
See also
America's #1 Health Problem, American Institute of Stress, http://www.stress.org/americas-1-health-problem/ (Accessed November 7, 2016).

17 "Stress Weakens the Immune System," American Psychological Association, http://www.apa.org/research/action/immune.aspx (Accessed September 7, 2016).

18 Jessica Ortner, *The Tapping Solution for Weight Loss and Body Confidence: A Woman's Guide to Stressing Less, Weighing Less, and Loving More* (Carlsbad: Hay House, 2014), 5.

Acknowledgments

A book is never written in isolation. As the authors, we would like to thank all the people who made this book possible through their support, encouragement, and time.

We'd like to thank all the college students who responded to our survey. Your answers provided the guidance we needed as we outlined the book and completed the scripts.

We'd also like to thank Pamela Graesser at Rivier University for allowing us the opportunity to speak and introduce Emotional Freedom Techniques, or EFT, to the Rivier students.

To our college beta readers, we thank you for all of your work and feedback. Thanks especially to Ellie Loconte, Margo Doyle, Zeina Zayat, and Shannon Amrein. Your time, effort, and feedback helped to make this a better and more useful book.

We'd like offer a special thanks to Diane Badzinski for editing the book and adding a professional overview of our written material.

A very special thanks to Margaret M. Lynch for taking her time to read the book and write a foreword. We are honored to have your words in our book.

To our reviewers, we offer a very special thank for your time reading and recommending the book through your testimonials.

We'd like to thank Chris O'Byrne at JETLAUNCH for his expert formatting of the print and digital versions of the book as well as his guidance throughout the publishing process.

Becki's Acknowledgements

To Brian, Toby and Josey for supporting me in everything I do, every day.

To my parents, through birth and marriage, Roland, Mary Jean, Bill, Helen, and John, and my siblings, Missy, Phillip, and Tara, for their support and love...I'd especially like to acknowledge my Mom, who did an AMAZING job editing our first draft. Her advice and knowledge was invaluable to us in so many ways.

To Kelley for being an amazing friend, colleague and co-author. Your knowledge of writing and publishing has taught me so much. I never would have been able to do this without you at my side, nor would I have wanted to...

To my friends for being "guinea pigs" and tapping with me while I was getting certified. Thank you all for your trust and encouragement.

To Ingrid Dinter for training me in how to use this amazing tool called Emotional Freedom Techniques in my coaching practice. Without your guidance, I would not have the success I have today.

Thank you to Jenny Bruck for inviting me to be a part of her amazing team at SCC Chiropractic & Vitality Studio. You are an inspiration!

To all the college students out there who believe in themselves enough to look outside of the box to find a new way to handle the stressors of college. With EFT, you now have a lifelong tool at your fingertips.

Kelley's Acknowledgements

To my family for all of their love and support. With you I laugh the hardest, love the deepest, and live the fullest.

Thank you to my husband Jim for listening and encouraging me in everything I do. Thanks to Andrew, Shannon, and Jonathon for being the best kids any mom could ask for. And for providing a wealth of college-related scenarios for a book about EFT and college stress.

To my parents, Dick and Linda, for a lifetime of support and love. You always told me I can do anything and this is the next step. A special thanks to my mom for all the writing pointers over the years. I certainly know where I acquired my love of words.

Thanks to my brother, Alex, who provides comic support exactly when needed. I love you.

To the Amrein family, who accepted me and welcomed me. I am honored to be a part of this family for... well a long time.

Many thanks to Jasmine Bharathan, from Mumbai, India, who first introduced me to EFT in 2007 and set me on a course of learning and discovery about this amazing tool.

To Becki, my co-author and friend, I'm so glad for your presence in my life. We were meant to meet and work together. We're a great team and writing this book has been an adventure I'd never have missed. We've got more to do and I know we're ready.

Ingrid Dinter, you've been a wonderful coach and mentor and I am thankful that I discovered your EFT training, so close to home, in 2014. Your inspiration continues to encourage my efforts on my own EFT journey.

I'd like to thank my friends, family and clients who have trusted me to facilitate their EFT tapping experiences. I have loved working with all of you and look forward to the opportunity to meet and work with new clients, as I continue to share EFT.

To all the college students who read and use this book, I offer my sincere thanks for your trust in the book and the process. EFT is the easiest way I've found to re-claim a place of calm and balance and I wish this for you as you navigate the college landscape. I do believe that twenty minutes of tapping a day is all it takes to make a profound difference in how you experience the stresses of life.

44971544R00133

Made in the USA
Middletown, DE
21 June 2017